Thank you...

C000081935

… for purchasing this copy of Reading for Literacy for ages 10-11. We hope that you find our worksheets, teachers' notes and display materials helpful as part of your programme of literacy activities.

Please note that photocopies can only be made for use by the purchasing institution. Supplying copies to other schools, institutions or individuals breaches the copyright licence. Thank you for your help in this.

This Reading for Literacy book is part of our growing range of educational titles. Most of our books are individual workbooks but, due to popular demand, we are now introducing a greater number of photocopiable titles especially for teachers. You may like to look out for:

READING FOR LITERACY for Reception
and for ages 5-7, 7-8, 8-9, 9-10, 10-11

WRITING FOR LITERACY for ages 5-7, 7-8, 8-9, 9-10, 10-11

SPELLING FOR LITERACY for ages 5-7, 7-8, 8-9, 9-10, 10-11

NUMERACY TODAY for ages 5-7, 7-9, 9-11

HOMEWORK TODAY for ages 7-8, 8-9, 9-10, 10-11

BEST HANDWRITING for ages 7-11

To find details of our other publications, please visit our website: **www.andrewbrodie.co.uk**

© Andrew Brodie Publications ✓ PO Box 23, Wellington, Somerset, TA21 8YX ✓ www.andrewbrodie.co.uk

ABOUT THIS BOOK

As with all our photocopiable resource books we have kept the teachers' notes to a minimum as we are well aware that teachers will use their own professionalism in using our materials.

At the start of each Unit we list some of the National Literacy Strategy Objectives that the Unit may cover. We are grateful to the Department for Education and Skills for their permission to quote the Objectives.

Some of the Units are linked to others as indicated by their titles.

Many Units feature reading activities that can be undertaken individually or in a small group situation, alongside the teacher or support assistant.

Some Units could be copied onto Overhead Projector Transparencies for use with a large group or the whole class.

The Units vary in their level of difficulty and teachers will match Units to the ability levels of the pupils in their classes.

Most Units are four pages long. All of them provide worthwhile activities as well as useful practice for tests.

Extracts from the National Literacy Strategy Framework for Teaching, © Crown copyright 1998, reproduced by kind permission of the Department for Education and Skills.

Contents ...
Year 6

Term 1

Unit 1   **Jennifer and Amy**

Objective 2   Different points of view

Unit 2   **Charlie**

Objective 2   To take account of viewpoint

Unit 3   **Lightning Strikes**

Objective 3   Personal responses to literature

Unit 4   **The Adventures of Robinson Crusoe**

Objective 4   Familiarity with an established author

Unit 5   **The Green Mamba**

Objective 4   Familiarity with an established author

Unit 6   **Champions League Football and Steve's Success**

Objective 11   Fact, opinion and fiction

Unit 7   **The Story of New Lanark and Aeroplanes**

Objective 11   Biography and autobiography

Unit 8   **Pennydown Primary School Survey Report**

Objective 13   Non-chronological reports

Unit 9   **The Three Witches (Macbeth)**

Range   Study of a Shakespeare play

Contents ...

Year 6

Term 2

Unit 10   **Strawberries**

Objective 1   Aspects of narrative structure

Unit 11   **Waves**

Objective 3   How poets manipulate words

Unit 12   **Investigating Humorous Verse**

Objective 4   The appeal of humorous verse

Unit 13   **Nonsense Poems**

Objective 4   Nonsense words

Unit 14   **Emily Brontë**

Objective 5   Messages, moods and feelings in poetry

Unit 15   **Four Great Poets**

Objective 6   Read and interpret poems

Unit 16   **Smoking**

Objective 15   Construction of an argument

Unit 17   **Reading the Small Print**

Objective 17   Use of official language

© Andrew Brodie Publications ✓ PO Box 23, Wellington, Somerset, TA21 8YX ✓ www.andrewbrodie.co.uk

Contents ...
Year 6

Term 3

Unit 18   **Moon Poems**

Objective 2   How linked poems relate to one another

Unit 19   **Snakes**

Objective 3   Evaluate the style of an individual poet

Unit 20   **Comparing Texts**

Objective 6   Contrast the work of different writers

Unit 21   **The Church at Thorne St Margaret**

Objective 15   Features of explanatory text

Unit 22   **New Lanark 2**

Objective 16   Impersonal formal language

Unit 23   **Forty Fabulous Facts**

Objective 17   Information retrieval

Unit 24   **More from Weather Watch**

Objective 19   Range of non-fiction text types

The objective indicated on the contents pages, is the main focus for each Unit. Each Unit can, however, be used for many different objectives and further suggestions of objectives are found at the start of each Unit.

This unit addresses the Literacy Strategy:
Term 1 objective 2: to take account of viewpoint in a novel through, e.g. identify the narrator; explaining how this influences the reader's view of events; explaining how events might look from a different point of view.
Term 1 objective 3: to articulate personal responses to literature, identifying why and how a text affects the reader.
Term 1 objective 5: to contribute constructively to shared discussion about literature, responding to and building on the views of others.
Term 2 objective 8: to analyse the success of texts and writers in evoking particular responses in the reader, e.g. where suspense is well-built.

Jennifer and Amy

The landscape views flashed past the windows of the train as Jennifer sat in a state of deep thought. Staring at the other passengers in the carriage in turn, she created a life for them all. They were allocated jobs, husbands, wives, children, homes. In their pockets she gave them all return tickets; they would journey away but return to their familiar lives today, tomorrow or next week.

Jennifer had nothing in common with these people. She had no family she knew, no home of her own and a single ticket. Fear and emptiness were the words that most accurately described her feelings. At 09.05 this morning her past life was left behind forever. She had always wanted a brother or sister but never more so than now. With her parents gone she was alone. She sat upright not resting on the back of the seat, gripping the ruck-sack on her lap. Through an advertisement in 'The Times' a cousin of her mother's had been found in London and it was at Paddington the train was due to arrive in 5 minutes.

Amy stood next to her mother shivering on the station platform. It was not cold but she was slightly nervous and excited at the same time.

"Do you think she'll like us?" Amy asked.

"It's bound to be difficult for her at first," replied her mother. "She'll be grieving for her parents for a long time and it will be up to us to try and help her make a new life."

"It was lucky we had a spare room in our house. It looks much better now we've decorated it and, once Jennifer has put her things in, it will feel more like home for her. I've always wanted a sister and now it will be like having one. We're going to be great friends."

They stood in silence again, each of them thinking of the first words they would say to their newly discovered relative.

Name _____ Jennifer and Amy

Comprehension

Choose the best word or group of
words which completes each
sentence accurately. Put a ring
around your choice.

1. Jennifer was sitting

    (in a bus.) (**in a train.**) (on the platform.) (in a car.)

2. She was

    (alone in the carriage.) (with her family.) (**with other people in the carriage.**)

3. Jennifer was feeling

    (happy and excited.) (**frightened and alone.**) (confident.)

4. Amy was waiting with

    (**her mother.**) (Jennifer.) (her father.)

5. She lives in a (flat.) (**house.**)

    Write true or false in the box.

6. Jennifer knew the other passengers.

True or False
false

7. Find and copy a phrase which tells you how Amy was feeling.

    She was slightly nervous and ~~extited~~ excited at
    the same time.

© Andrew Brodie Publications ✓ PO Box 23, Wellington, Somerset, TA21 8YX ✓ www.andrewbrodie.co.uk

Identifying a Viewpoint

The passage called Jennifer and Amy is the
beginning of a story about two girls who are going
to meet for the first time. They each have different
feelings about the event. Jennifer feels frightened
and empty. Look at the first part of the passage
again and explain why you think she felt like this.

Jennifer is moving in with pea peo people she had
never met, and she didn't have her parents with her.

Think about Amy's point of view. If you
were having a relative you had not met
coming to live with you, would you feel the
same as Amy? Explain your answer.

I would not enjoy it.
It would be different with someone I know
but having someone you never met moving in
would be would be very strange even is it were
was a relative.

© Andrew Brodie Publications ✓ PO Box 23, Wellington, Somerset, TA21 8YX ✓ www.andrewbrodie.co.uk

Underline 2 of the following words
which most accurately describe
Jennifer's feelings.

thoughtful   **cheerful**

anxious   **optimistic**

The passage was set in 2 different locations; where were they?

1   The train to paddington station.

2   Paddington station.

How do we know that the 1st and 2nd parts of the passage were set at about the same time?

The two girls were were waiting to meet each other.

© Andrew Brodie Publications ✓ PO Box 23, Wellington, Somerset, TA21 8YX ✓ www.andrewbrodie.co.uk

This unit addresses the Literacy Strategy:
Term 1 objective   2: to take account of viewpoint in a novel through e.g. identify the narrator; explaining how this influences the reader's view
                    of events; explaining how events might look from a different point of view.
Term 1 objective   5: to contribute constructively to shared discussion about literature, responding to and building on the views of others.

Charlie

Charlie sat on his usual seat in the coach. Not in the front where the keen people sat, not at the back where the rebels sat, but bang in the middle where he hoped he wouldn't be noticed.

It didn't work of course. Just like every week the twins, Wayne and Shane, tousled his neatly-combed hair on their way to the back seat. Just like every week their girlfriends, Hannah and Carly, giggled at him unkindly and went to join Wayne and Shane.

Webster was in a bad mood. He'd barked the register at them before they'd left school and hadn't smiled his usual sickening grimace to Hannah and Carly when they'd offered to take the register to the office. If Webster wasn't even nice to Hannah and Carly, how was he going to be to Charlie today?

Webster's moods didn't bear thinking about so Charlie gazed out of the window and watched the drizzle and the people in the street huddled inside their coats to keep warm. All except Wayne and Shane Johnson's dad that is. Just like every week Mr Johnson was standing outside his garage as they went past, wearing his tough-guy teeshirt despite the drizzle and the cold. He waved and grinned at Wayne and Shane who waved and grinned back.

The coach pulled up at the swimming pool and Charlie cheered up. He had to walk past Webster and he had to change in the changing room but, even so, he loved swimming.

"You can wipe that smile off your face Smith!" shouted Webster. "There's no fun for you today, that's for sure."

Name _____ Charlie

Comprehension

Read the passage carefully to answer the questions below.
Draw a ring around the correct answer:

1. Charlie is going

    (shopping.)   (skating.)   (skiing.)   (swimming.)

2. Webster is a

    (bus driver.)   (teacher.)   (swimming instructor.)   (pupil.)

3. How many adults are mentioned in the passage?

    (2)   (4)   (5)   (6)

4. How many children are mentioned by name in the passage?

    (2)   (4)   (5)   (6)

5. Charlie's surname is

    (Webster.)   (Smith.)   (Johnson.)   (Carly.)

6. Which of these statements could best describe Mr Webster as
    Charlie sees him?
    Tick one box.

    Mr Webster is friendly and cheerful. ☐

    Mr Webster is unfriendly and grumpy. ☐

    Mr Webster smiles a lot. ☐

    Mr Webster is pleased when Charlie smiles. ☐

7. Charlie is going for a swimming lesson. Which paragraph shows us
    this? Put a ring around your choice.

    1st   2nd   3rd   4th   5th   6th

© Andrew Brodie Publications ✓ PO Box 23, Wellington, Somerset, TA21 8YX ✓ www.andrewbrodie.co.uk

8. Give a brief description of the weather conditions when Charlie was on his way to swimming.

_____

_____

_____

_____

9. Do you think that Mr Johnson was dressed appropriately for the weather? Give a reason for your answer.

_____

_____

10. How can we tell that Mr Webster was not in a good mood on the morning of the swimming lesson? Look for more than one piece of evidence.

_____

_____

_____

_____

_____

_____

11. One phrase is repeated three times in the passage. What is this phrase?

_____

12. Charlie has a mixture of feelings on the morning of the swimming lesson. Explain his different feelings.

_____

_____

_____

_____

_____

_____

© Andrew Brodie Publications ✓ PO Box 23, Wellington, Somerset, TA21 8YX ✓ www.andrewbrodie.co.uk

13. How do you think the other characters view Charlie?
Write a short description of Charlie from Wayne's point of view.

_____

_____

_____

_____

14. Now write a short description of Charlie from Hannah's point of view.

_____

_____

_____

_____

_____

_____

_____

15. What happened next?
Make up the next part of the story.

_____

_____

_____

_____

_____

_____

_____

_____

_____

_____

_____

_____

This unit addresses the Literacy Strategy:
Term 1 objective 2: to take account of viewpoint in a novel through, e.g. identify the narrator; explaining how this influences the reader's view of events, explaining how events might look from a different point of view.
Term 1 objective 3: to articulate personal responses to literature, identifying why and how a text affects the reader.
Term 1 objective 5: to contribute constructively to shared discussion about literature, responding to and building on the views of others.
Term 1 objective 11: to distinguish between biography and autobiography: recognising the effect on the reader of the choice between first and third person; distinguishing between fact, opinion and fiction;distinguishing between implicit and explicit points of view and how these can differ.

Enjoy reading this magazine article.

It is from a magazine for young people. It is called 'Weather Watch."

LIGHTNING STRIKES

It was a calm June day and Meera was playing in the small square garden outside the little house by the river. It was an idyllic setting, seemingly a million miles away from the humdrum world of everyday life. A perfect place for a holiday, thought Meera as she fed tiny pieces of stale bread to the ducks.

Sanjeev, her brother, came out of the bright blue painted door. At twelve, he was two years Meera's senior and, she felt, he was very bossy.

"Let's walk Max," Sanjeev suggested. Max was their dog, nearly as old as Sanjeev, so whilst partial to a walk, he liked to amble along slowly.

"OK," said Meera, "I'll fetch a lead."

The two children and their dog went through the back gate and wandered along the grassy path that led to the marshes. Max snuffled along, delighting in all the interesting new smells he was encountering. The children looked at the cottages, boats and windmills, sights so very different from near their home in the city.

After about ten minutes they were suddenly aware of ominous black clouds gathering in the sky that had seemed a perfect cornflower blue such a short time ago.

The singing of the birds ceased, and, as if from nowhere, large cool drops of rain began to fall on them. Almost immediately the rain seemed to be dropping like a solid curtain around them, and they were all getting very wet. In the distance a long low rumble of thunder could be heard.

"I think we should shelter," said Sanjeev, in his 'I'm older than you, and I know best' voice.

"Where?" asked Meera.

"Under the tree over there we should be fairly dry."

"But I'm sure that sheltering under a tree isn't wise in a storm," argued Meera.

"Well there's nowhere else and the thunder sounded a long way away, so unless you have a better idea, let's get out of this downpour," insisted her brother.

© Andrew Brodie Publications ✓ PO Box 23, Wellington, Somerset, TA21 8YX ✓ www.andrewbrodie.co.uk

"If we must," agreed Meera miserably.
As they neared the tree, they stopped, for there, standing beneath it they saw figures. Indistinctly, shimmering through the torrents of rain, were what looked like two children about the same age as themselves waving frantically and shaking their heads. Their lips were moving but there was no sound. Meera thought they seemed to be noiselessly shouting, "NO, DON'T COME NEAR!"

These strange apparitions made the children hesitate in disbelief - they had seen no-one else on the path, so how could anyone possibly be there?

A few seconds later the figures simply vanished.

"What shall we do?" asked Meera, the rain running uncomfortably down her face and dripping from her nose and chin.

For once her brother had no answer. They couldn't both have imagined the same thing, could they?

A moment later there was an ear-splitting crack, as a vicious streak of yellow lightning struck the tree. To their horror it fell to the ground in the place they would have been standing, had they sheltered beneath its branches.

Two very shaken children, and a soggy brown dog, ran wordlessly all the way back to their holiday home. Dad was by the back gate watching anxiously for them.

"You're soaked," he said, "go in and get dry and changed, whilst I dry Max."

When they were warm and dry the children told their tale to their incredulous parents, who eventually smiled benignly and attributed the ghostly figures to their children's over-active imagination.

The figures beneath the tree had warned the children of the impending danger, and saved their lives. Meera and Sanjeev know they hadn't imagined it. Or had they? Perhaps no one would ever know.

Read 'Weather Watch' next week and find out what had happened three hundred years earlier in the very spot that Meera and Sanjeev nearly sheltered.

When you have answered the questions about Lightning Strikes...

...you can read some more extracts from Weather Watch.

© Andrew Brodie Publications ✓ PO Box 23, Wellington, Somerset, TA21 8YX ✓ www.andrewbrodie.co.uk

Basic Comprehension

⚡ Write three words from the text that mean the opposite of large.

_____   _____   _____

⚡ Where were the children taking the dog?

_____

_____

⚡ What did they see on the way?

_____

_____

⚡ Would you consider 'Lightning Strikes' to be **fact**, **opinion** or **fiction**?

_____

⚡ What age is Meera in the story?   _____

⚡ Write four words that are used with the dialogue instead of the word '**said**'.

_____   _____   _____   _____

⚡ What colour are cornflowers?   _____

⚡ Write the sentence in the text that gave you that information.

_____

_____

_____

_____

⚡ Write the phrase that describes the lightning.

_____

⚡ Why do you think Dad was 'watching anxiously' for them.

_____

_____

_____

⚡ **Read the story again carefully, then on the back of the sheet do a detailed picture of the scene from the story. Write a caption for your picture.**

© Andrew Brodie Publications ✓ PO Box 23, Wellington, Somerset, TA21 8YX ✓ www.andrewbrodie.co.uk

Advanced Comprehension

⚡ Read the story carefully and invent what you consider to be a more effective title.

_____

⚡ Give reasons for your choice of title.

_____

_____

_____

⚡ Who would you consider to be the main character in the story and why?

_____   _____

_____

⚡ Write a definition for each of the following words found in the story.

ominous _____

_____

idyllic _____

_____

amble _____

_____

apparitions _____

_____

incredulous _____

_____

benignly _____

_____

With a partner, discuss ways in which you think you could improve the story.

Consider these points   - ways to build suspense;
- effective story endings;
- the readers' views of the characters;
- effective use of descriptive language.

Make notes of your ideas to share with the class.

Rewrite the story making a different character the central one. You may even consider writing it in the first person, telling the story as if you were that central character.

© Andrew Brodie Publications ✓ PO Box 23, Wellington, Somerset, TA21 8YX ✓ www.andrewbrodie.co.uk

This unit addresses the Literacy Strategy:
Term 1 objective 2: to take account of viewpoint in a novel through, e.g.identify the narrator; explaining how this influences the reader's view of events; explaining how events might look from a different point of view.
Term 1 objective 4: to be familiar with the work of some established authors, to know what is special about their work, and to explain their preferences in terms of authors, styles and themes.
Term 1 objective 5: to contribute to shared discussion about literature, responding to and building on the views of others.
Term 2 objective 9: to increase familiarity with significant poets and writers of the past.

The Adventures of Robinson Crusoe
by Daniel Defoe

The author Daniel Defoe wrote this story in the early 18th century.

This was the first 'desert island' story and has been the inspiration for many others.

This extract begins when Robinson Crusoe has just been washed up on the island, and realises he is the only survivor.

I walked about on the shore, lifting up my hands, and my whole being, as I may say, wrapt up in the contemplation of my deliverance, making a thousand gestures and motions which I cannot describe, reflecting upon all my comrades that were drowned, and that there should not be one soul saved but myself; for, as for them, I never saw them afterwards, or any sign of them, except three of their hats, one cap, and two shoes that were not fellows.

I cast my eyes to the stranded vessel, when the breach and froth of the sea being so big, I could hardly see it, it lay so far off, and considered, Lord! How was it possible I could get on shore?

After I had solaced my mind with the comfortable part of my condition, I began to look round me to see what kind of place I was in, and what was next to be done, and I soon found my comforts abate, and that, in a word, I had a dreadful deliverance; for I was wet, had no clothes to shift me, nor anything either to eat or drink to comfort me, neither did I see any prospect before me but that of perishing with hunger, or being devoured by wild beasts; and that which was particularly afflicting to me was that I had no weapon either to hunt and kill any creature for my sustenance, or to defend myself against any other creature that might desire to kill me for theirs. In a word, I had nothing about me but a knife, a tobacco-pipe, and a little tobacco in a box. This was all my provision; and this threw me into terrible agonies of mind, that for a while I ran about like a madman. Night coming upon me, I began, with a heavy heart, to consider what would be my lot if there were any ravenous beasts in that country, seeing at night they always come abroad for their prey.

All the remedy that offered to my thoughts at that time was, to get up into a thick bushy tree like a fir, but thorny, which grew near me, and where I resolved to sit all night, and consider the next day what death I should die, for as yet I saw no prospect of life. I walked about a furlong from the shore, to see if I could find any fresh water to drink, which I did, to my great joy; and having drank, and put a little tobacco in my mouth to prevent hunger, I went to the tree, and getting up into it, endeavoured to place myself so, as that if I should sleep I might not fall; and having cut me a short stick, like a truncheon, for my defence, I took up my lodging, and having been excessively fatigued, I fell fast asleep, and slept as comfortably as, I believe, few could have done in my condition, and found myself the most refreshed with it that I think I ever was on such an occasion.

When I waked it was broad day, the weather clear, and the storm abated, so that the sea did not rage and swell as before. But that which surprised me most was, that the ship was lifted off in the night from the sand where she lay, by the swelling of the tide, and was driven up almost as far as the rock which I first mentioned, where I had been so bruised by the sea dashing me against it. This being within about a mile from the shore where I was, and the ship seeming to stand upright still, I wished myself on board, that, at least, I might have some necessary things for my use.

When I came down from my apartment in the tree I looked about me again, and the first thing I found was the boat, which lay as the wind and the sea had tossed her up upon the land, about two miles on my right hand. I walked as far as I could upon the shore to have got to her, but found a neck or inlet of water between me and the boat, which was about half a mile broad; so I came back for the present, being more intent upon getting at the ship, where I hoped to find something for my present subsistence.

If you enjoy adventure stories you should try reading the whole of the Robinson Crusoe story.

Perhaps you could compare the story with one of the many films about being stranded on a desert island.

© Andrew Brodie Publications ✓ PO Box 23, Wellington, Somerset, TA21 8YX ✓ www.andrewbrodie.co.uk

Basic Comprehension

1.   Find two words in the text, that are used to describe any 'fierce beasts' that Robinson Crusoe feared he might meet.

_____   _____

2.   How many characters appear in the extract?   _____

3.   In the second paragraph what word is used instead of ship?

_____

4.   Which is the word that tells us the ship is unable to move from its position?

_____

5.   Write the sentence from the text that tells you what the weather was like on Robinson Crusoe's second day on the island.

_____

_____

_____

_____

6.   Write two words that mean the same as '**excessively fatigued**'.

_____

7.   Make a list of ten items that you think would be most important to have if you were stranded on a desert island. These must all be items small enough to carry - so not luxury hotels or jet aircraft!

_____   _____

_____   _____

_____   _____

_____   _____

_____   _____

8. Who is narrating the story?   _____

9. Why do you think the story is written in this way?

_____

_____

© Andrew Brodie Publications ✓ PO Box 23, Wellington, Somerset, TA21 8YX ✓ www.andrewbrodie.co.uk

Advanced Comprehension

10. Write a word that means the same (or nearly the same) as each of the words below.

The words can all be found in the text so reading them in context may help you with this; or of course you may need to use a thesaurus.

contemplation	**solaced**
deliverance	**comrades**
devoured	**abated**
subsistence	**dashing**

11. Explain the meaning of the phrase ' two shoes that were not fellows'.

_____

_____

12. Why did Robinson Crusoe choose to sleep in a tree?

_____

_____

_____

13. On the back of the sheet rewrite the first paragraph in the third person and in modern English.

You may need to reconstruct some sentences to make them sound up-to-date.

14. Compare your results with those of a friend. Discuss reasons for the differences.

15. Daniel Defoe used extremely long sentences! Reread the passage and try to find the longest sentence. Count the number of words in the sentence. Now choose a page in your own reading book and find the longest sentence. Count the number of words in that sentence so you can make a comparison.

© Andrew Brodie Publications ✓ PO Box 23, Wellington, Somerset, TA21 8YX ✓ www.andrewbrodie.co.uk

This unit addresses the Literacy Strategy:
Term 1 objective   2: to take account of viewpoint in a novel through, e.g.. identify the narrator; explaining how this influences the reader's view of events; explaining how events might look from a different point of view.
Term 1 objective   4: to be familiar with the work of some established authors, to know what is special about their work, and to explain their preferences in terms of authors, styles and themes.
Term 1 objective   5: to contribute constructively to shared discussion about literature, responding to and building on the views of others.
Term 2 objective   9: to increase familiarity with significant poets and writers of the past.

Extract from   **Roald Dahl - Going Solo**

Chapter 4 - **The Green Mamba**

Oh, those snakes! How I hated them! They were the only fearful thing about Tanganyika, and a newcomer very quickly learnt to identify most of them and to know which were deadly and which were simply poisonous. The killers, apart from the black mambas, were the green mambas, the cobras and the tiny little puff adders that looked very much like small sticks lying motionless in the middle of a dusty path, and so easy to step on.

One Sunday evening I was invited to go and have a sundowner at the house of an Englishman called Fuller who worked in the Customs office in Dar es Salaam. He lived with his wife and two small children in a plain white wooden house that stood alone some way back from the road in a rough grassy piece of ground with coconut trees scattered about. I was walking across the grass towards the house and was about twenty yards away when I saw a large green snake go gliding straight up the veranda steps of Fuller's house and in through the open front door. The brilliant yellowy-green skin and its great size made me certain it was a green mamba, a creature almost as deadly as the black mamba, and for a few seconds I was so startled and dumbfounded and horrified that I froze to the spot. Then I pulled myself together and ran round to the back of the house shouting, "Mr Fuller! Mr Fuller!"

Extract from 'Going Solo' by Roald Dahl, published by Jonathan Cape Ltd and Penguin Books Ltd. Reproduced by kind permission of David Higham Associates.

Comprehension

For the following sections you will need to refer to the extract from 'Going Solo' by Roald Dahl. This extract forms the start of a chapter called 'The Green Mamba'.

Put a ring around the word or group of words which you think answers the question most accurately.

1. How did the narrator feel about snakes?

(He likes them.)   (He hates them.)

2. According to the text, in Tanganyika how many different types of snakes could kill you?

(one)   (two)   (three)   (four)   (five)

3. Put a ring around three of the following words which could be used to describe Mr Fuller's house.

(brick)   (white)   (detached)   (green)   (wooden)

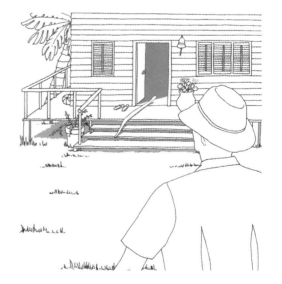

4. There are three words in the text which tell us how the narrator felt when he saw the green mamba.
    What are they?

    1. _____
    2. _____
    3. _____

5. How was the author certain it was a green mamba?

_____

_____

_____

_____

© Andrew Brodie Publications ✓ PO Box 23, Wellington, Somerset, TA21 8YX ✓ www.andrewbrodie.co.uk

Further Comprehension

6.   Identify the narrator in the passage called 'The Green Mamba'.

_____

_____

7.   Ring the correct answer.   The passage is

autobiographical   biographical

8.   List at least three things that the first paragraph does to set the scene for the second paragraph.

1. _____

_____

_____

2. _____

_____

_____

3. _____

_____

_____

9.   How do you know that the narrator is not a native of Tanganyika?

_____

_____

_____

10.   The country in which the story is set is no longer called Tanganyika. Try to find out what it is now called, then find some information about the country. Write two sentences about it here:

_____

_____

_____

_____

© Andrew Brodie Publications ✓ PO Box 23, Wellington, Somerset, TA21 8YX ✓ www.andrewbrodie.co.uk

11. What do you learn about the climate in Tanganyika from reading the text? Use two extracts from the text in your answer.

_____

_____

_____

_____

_____

_____

_____

_____

_____

_____

12. Summarise each paragraph in the extract down to three main points.

Paragraph 1.

(i) _____

_____

(ii) _____

_____

(iii) _____

_____

Paragraph 2.

(i) _____

_____

(ii) _____

_____

(iii) _____

_____

© Andrew Brodie Publications ✓ PO Box 23, Wellington, Somerset, TA21 8YX ✓ www.andrewbrodie.co.uk

This unit addresses the Literacy Strategy:
Term 1 objective   11: to distinguish between biography and autobiography; to recognise the effect on the reader of the choice between first and third person; distinguishing between fact, opinion and fiction; distinguishing between implicit points of view and how these can differ.
Term 3 objective   19: to review a range of non-fiction text types and their characteristics, discussing when a writer might choose to write in a given style and form.

YEAR	UNIT	Sheet
6	6	A

Name

Fact, Opinion and Fiction

Champions League Football

Manchester United played Bayern Munich on the evening of March 13th at Old Trafford. Old Trafford is Manchester United's home ground. The match was a goalless draw. The fight for first position in Group A of the league is still evenly balanced. United need only to match Bayern's result next week to take first position. The Germans, however, have an easier final game at home against Nantes, who are bottom of the group at the moment. The English will have to travel away to Boavista for their game.

Manchester United	0
Bayern Munich	0

GROUP A

RESULTS	Man U 0	Bayern M 0
	Nantes 1	Boavista 1
FIXTURES 19TH MARCH	Bayern M V Nantes	
	Boavista V Man U	

Manchester United 0   Bayern Munich 0

Manchester United let themselves down yesterday in the match against Bayern Munich. They missed several chances at goal; the closest was a shot by Giggs who skillfully wound the ball down the pitch through Bayern's defence and kicked at goal with his right foot, but it went wide. Had he transferred the ball to his left foot, which he favours, he would probably have been lucky.

The first half of the game was uninspiring - both teams failed to show us their best play. The second half was more exciting with both teams desperate to break into the lead. Bayern's goalkeeper did well to stop a shot from Van Nistelrooy close to the end.

by Larry Porter

© Andrew Brodie Publications ✓ PO Box 23, Wellington, Somerset, TA21 8YX ✓ www.andrewbrodie.co.uk

Steve's Success

by Andrew Brodie

Steve loved football. He never missed a practice at school; it was his favourite time of the week. He found most of his school work difficult, especially if it involved writing. He always worked hard but never seemed to do as well as his class mates.

But football was different. The harder he tried, the better he got.

Mrs Watts, the teacher who took football club, noticed Steve from the start. He could control the ball and kick accurately and, most importantly in her view, he understood what being a team player meant.

Steve was eleven but had the skill of a much older boy. Steve had talents that were too good to ignore. Mrs Watts searched the internet and found a website with information about 'sports schools' where young people, who excel in a particular sport, can have the best training possible. The teacher contacted Steve's parents and, with their permission, e-mailed details about Steve.

A month or so later, Steve was at football practice as usual. On the sideline with Mrs Watts was a track-suited man watching the game with keen interest. As the practice went on the man got more and more enthusiastic, shouting praise and advice to all the players, but particularly to Steve.

"Great game, well played," he said walking towards Steve.

"How would you like to have more training Steve? We have special training schools where you can come at the weekends and even stay for a week during the school holidays."

Steve thought this was the best moment of his life. His future in football had begun.

ANSWER SECTION

The three pieces of writing in this section are all on the subject of football. One is based on **fact**, one is **opinion** and the third is **fiction**.

(1) Sort the three pieces by putting the correct title against the labels below.

fiction:	_____
fact:	_____
opinion:	_____

© Andrew Brodie Publications ✓ PO Box 23, Wellington, Somerset, TA21 8YX ✓ www.andrewbrodie.co.uk

'Steve's Success'

(2) How do we know that the piece of writing called 'Steve's Success' is not autobiographical? You may be able to think of more than one answer.

_____

_____

_____

_____

_____

(3) Choose the best word or group of words which fit the story 'Steve's Success'. Put a ring around your choice.

○ Steve's favourite subject at school was

maths.   **writing.**   **football.**

○ Mrs Watts thought Steve was particularly good at

**keeping
the ball.**   **kicking
accurately.**   **playing as part
of a team.**   **running
fast.**

(4) ○ Why did Mrs Watts contact Steve's parents?

**to tell them how good
he was**   **to ask if it was all right to
contact a sports school about
Steve**   **to invite them to
watch a match**

(5) Which of these statements <u>best</u> describes Mrs Watts' views on Steve?
Tick ONE box.

Steve was not good at writing.   ☐

Steve acted older than his age.   ☐

Steve was an exceptionally talented football player.   ☐

**Steve should leave school and just play football at a
sports school.**   ☐

© Andrew Brodie Publications ✓ PO Box 23, Wellington, Somerset, TA21 8YX ✓ www.andrewbrodie.co.uk

Look again at the two pieces of writing called 'Champions' League Football' and 'Manchester United 0 Bayern Munich 0' by Larry Porter. The first piece is <u>fact.</u> It states what actually happened or will happen, whereas Larry Porter's article is his opinion of the game. It tells us what he thought about it. Someone else, who saw the match, may agree or disagree with him. His opinion can be challenged.

Write some notes about something you feel strongly about. This could be developed into a short piece of writing or a speaking and listening activity with a partner. Tell a partner your views and ask your partner to challenge your opinions. The role can then be reversed.

Some suggestions for topics you may have opinions on:

- ➤ Using animals for experiments
- ➤ Hunting with hounds
- ➤ School uniforms

_____

_____

_____

_____

_____

_____

_____

_____

_____

_____

_____

_____

This unit addresses the Literacy Strategy:
Term 1 objective 11: to distinguish between biography and autobiography; recognising the effect on the reader of the choice between first and
third person; distinguishing between fact, opinion and fiction; distinguishing between implicit and explicit points of view
and how these can differ.
Term 3 objective 17: to appraise text quickly and effectively, to retrieve information from it; to find information quickly and evaluate its value.

**Biography &
Autobiography**

Extract from 'The Story of New Lanark'
published by New Lanark Conservation Trust

Robert Owen's arrival at New Lanark begins a remarkable story brightly embroidered with romance: the romance of his courtship with David Dale's eldest daughter Caroline, the romance of his first instinct that here was the place in which to turn his dreams for social reform into reality, all this against the romantic backdrop of the village itself in its leafy setting by the Falls of Clyde.

Owen's name is recorded for the first time in the Visitors' Book at New Lanark in 1798. What had brought him there was a chance introduction to Caroline Dale in Glasgow. One senses that Caroline was attracted to the ambitious young Welshman from the start. Has Mr Owen, she asked, yet seen the beauties of the Falls of Clyde and her father's mills? If not, she could arrange introductions at New Lanark and would be most interested to hear his impressions of the place after the visit. They were to be strong ones. As he stood in front of New Lanark after an inspection of the mills, Owen declared: "Of all the places I have yet seen, I should prefer this in which to try an experiment I have long contemplated and have wished to have an opportunity to put into practice."

He was to have his chance sooner than he could have expected. According to his own later account, two developments proceeded in tandem: the romance with Caroline blossomed and rumours grew that Dale was looking for a buyer for New Lanark. Although infatuated by him, Caroline would not marry without her father's consent and the young suitor had yet to meet, let alone gain the approval of David Dale, who by now was one of the wealthiest and best-known businessmen in Glasgow. The idea occurred to Owen that an enquiry regarding the possible purchase of New Lanark would provide the necessary pretext for a meeting. Once again the Visitors' Book tells the story: another visit to the village by Owen himself following a further trip in the company of two prospective partners, John Barton of Manchester and John Atkinson of London, both well established in the business world. Dale's initial scepticism at the seriousness of the young-looking 27-year-old Owen was overcome – and New Lanark sold for £60,000. The Dale daughters remained that summer in the house that David Dale had built for the family in the centre of the village, and this provided Owen and Caroline with the opportunity to continue their courting on frequent walks along the Clyde. Dale himself, however, was hostile to the match. In the absence of a son he considered his eldest daughter was the appropriate person to continue his work. His preference for a husband for her was "an honest Scotchman."

Extract from 'The Story of New Lanark' reproduced by kind permission of the New Lanark Conservation Trust.

As you know, a description of the life of a person, written by another person, is called a biography. The extract from 'The Story of New Lanark' gives some biographical information about Robert Owen. Use this information to answer the questions below. Write your answers in full, clear, well-punctuated sentences.

What nationality was Owen?

_____

When did Owen first visit New Lanark?

_____

_____

Why did Owen first visit New Lanark?

_____

_____

_____

How old was Owen when he bought New Lanark with his business partners?

_____

_____

In what way did David Dale think that Owen was unsuitable to marry his daughter?

_____

_____

The author of the extract uses a particular word to describe Owen's character. a. Unscramble these letters to find the word.

i i m s o b u t a ⟶ [   ]

What does this word mean?   _____

_____

_____

Could you use this word to describe yourself? If so, in what ways?

_____

_____

_____

_____

© Andrew Brodie Publications ✓ PO Box 23, Wellington, Somerset, TA21 8YX ✓ www.andrewbrodie.co.uk

Aeroplanes

Not far from our house was a muddy track overhung with leafy branches. I don't know of anyone going along there apart from us, so, once we were through the shadows, we had to wade through undisturbed nettles as tall as our chests.

Past the nettles we reached our target: aeroplanes. Aeroplanes with wings to run along, cockpits to climb into, joysticks to pull and push and ease to left and right so that we too could be aces. We were the boys in blue of our green-leafed sky, Brylcreem boys of our muddy heavens. We were the leather-clad heart-throbs of the girls who would be waiting for us when we returned … to school on Monday.

The leather of the seats was torn. The glass of the windows was shattered into hundreds of small cube-shaped fragments. The wind and rain had dragged vegetation into the cockpit to soak and blacken. But, for us, the buttons at the top of the joystick still operated machine guns like we saw in the films. Tracer bullets still showed the trueness of our aim and, time after time, we brought down black-crossed Messerschmitts with our red and blue roundeled Spitfires and Hurricanes.

At the end of the day, we climbed wearily from our fighting machines, dragged ourselves through the now-bent nettles and returned home to share our bath and to wash away the smell that filled our nostrils. I can still smell it now – the smell of oil and damp and age and nostalgia.

© Andrew Brodie Publications ✓ PO Box 23, Wellington, Somerset, TA21 8YX ✓ www.andrewbrodie.co.uk

Name _____

Biography &
Autobiography

Is this piece of writing biographical or autobiographical? How can you tell? Give some examples from the text to support your view.

_____

_____

_____

_____

_____

_____

_____

_____

What is the meaning of the word nostalgia?
Find its definition in a dictionary.

Nostalgia: _____

_____

_____

_____

The word nostalgia is a noun; it is the name for a way of feeling. A related word is nostalgic which is an adjective. The writer of this passage is feeling nostalgic about playing on the aeroplanes when he was a boy.
Think about your own life so far. Try to remember what it was like to be a young child. Now try to describe a time in your life about which you feel nostalgic:

_____

_____

_____

_____

_____

_____

_____

_____

This could be part of your own autobiography.

© Andrew Brodie Publications ✓ PO Box 23, Wellington, Somerset, TA21 8YX ✓ www.andrewbrodie.co.uk

This unit addresses the Literacy Strategy:
Term 1 objective 13: to secure understanding of the features of non-chronological reports: - introductions to orientate reader; - use of generalisations to categorise; - language to describe and differentiate; - impersonal language; - mostly present tense.

Survey Report:
Classroom 7, Pennydown Primary School.

Classroom 7 is situated on the South side of the school. All external window frames are in need of repainting. Four of the windows require remedial treatment to replace rotten wood and to re-bed the glass in putty. On the day of the survey, heavy rain resulted in some water penetration of the three windows in the south-west corner of the room. Severe dripping caused saturation of the carpet.

Some pooling of water occurs on the flat roof. I was unable to inspect the roof surface thoroughly due to the inclement weather conditions. However evidence of leakage on the interior ceiling would indicate that the felted and stoned roof is in need of some repair. Minor roof repairs were carried out some eight years ago but, prior to that, the roof has received no attention since the school was constructed in 1978. The ceiling itself has brown stains where water has soaked into the fibre-board tiles. Again, on the day of the survey, some water was penetrating into the classroom and the teacher had moved one group of children so that buckets could be placed to catch the drips. These children were required to work in the corridor which is poorly lit and lacks insulation and heating.

The interior of the classroom has not been decorated for some time. Complete internal redecoration of the school took place in 1992 and the headteacher remembers that a teacher painted this classroom during the summer holidays approximately five years ago. The skirtings and door frames are now extensively chipped. Window frames are still, in the main, well coated in gloss but peeling has taken place where water has penetrated.

The floor covering largely consists of carpet which is threadbare in places and constitutes a trip hazard.

Bill Jenkins
District Surveyor

© Andrew Brodie Publications ✓ PO Box 23, Wellington, Somerset, TA21 8YX ✓ www.andrewbrodie.co.uk

Basic Comprehension

1. What is the job title of the person who wrote the report?

   _____

2. What is the name of the school?

   _____

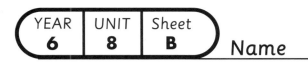

3. Which classroom is being inspected?

   _____

4. When was the school built?

   _____

5. How many years old was the school when all the classrooms were redecorated?

   _____

6. Which external features of the building did the surveyor comment on?

   _____

   _____

7. Which internal features of the classroom did the surveyor comment on?

   _____

   _____

8. Are there any aspects of the internal condition of the classroom that the surveyor did not comment on? (Look around your own classroom.)

   _____

   _____

   _____

   _____

   _____

   _____

   _____

   _____

© Andrew Brodie Publications ✓ PO Box 23, Wellington, Somerset, TA21 8YX ✓ www.andrewbrodie.co.uk

Survey Report

9. Which aspect of the classroom's condition was dangerous?

    _____

    _____

10. Why was the corridor an unsuitable place for the children to work?

    _____

    _____

    _____

11. How would you summarise the condition of the classroom described in the report?

    _____

    _____

    _____

    _____

Verb Tenses

Reread the passage. Examine the verbs carefully as you read. Draw a blue line under all the verbs that are written in the present tense. Draw a red line under all the verbs written in the past tense.

12. What is the surveyor describing when he uses verbs in the present tense?

    _____

    _____

    _____

    _____

13. The surveyor uses the past tense for two aspects of his report.
    What are these two aspects?

    _____

    _____

    _____

    _____

© Andrew Brodie Publications ✓ PO Box 23, Wellington, Somerset, TA21 8YX ✓ www.andrewbrodie.co.uk

Look carefully at your own classroom. Is it in good condition or poor condition? Perhaps some features of the room are good while others are poor. Write a report about your classroom, in the style of a building surveyor.

_____

This unit addresses the Literacy Strategy:
Term 1 objective   4: to be familiar with the work of some established authors, to know what is special about their work, and to explain their preferences in terms of authors, styles and themes

Macbeth Act 1 Scene 3. A Heath

Third Witch:	A drum, a drum!
	Macbeth doth come.
All witches:	The weird sisters, hand in hand,
	Posters of the sea and land,
	Thus do go about, about:
	Thrice to thine, and thrice to mine,
	And thrice again, to make up nine:-
	Peace! – the charm's wound up.

Enter Macbeth and Banquo

Macbeth:	So foul and fair a day I have not seen.
Banquo:	How far is't call'd to Forres? – What are these,
	So wither'd and so wild in their attire,
	They look not like the inhabitants o' the earth,
	And yet are on't? – Live you? or are you aught
	That man may question? You seem to understand me,
	By each at once her chappy finger laying upon her skinny lips:- you
	should be women, and yet your beards forbid me to interpret
	that you are so.
Macbeth:	Speak, if you can;- what are you?
First Witch:	All hail, Macbeth! hail to thee, Thane of Glamis!
Second Witch:	All hail, Macbeth! hail to thee, Thane of Cawdor!
Third Witch:	All hail, Macbeth! thou shalt be king hereafter!
Banquo:	Good sir, why do you start; and seem to fear things that do sound
	so fair? I'the name of truth, are you fantastical, or that indeed which
	outwardly ye show? My noble partner you greet with present grace
	and great prediction of noble having and of royal hope, that he
	seems rapt withal: - to me you speak not:
	If you can look into the seeds of time, and say which grain will sow,
	and which will not, speak then to me, who neither beg nor fear your
	favours nor your hate.
First Witch:	Hail!
Second Witch:	Hail!
Third Witch:	Hail!
First Witch:	Lesser than Macbeth, and greater.
Second Witch:	Not so happy, yet much happier.
Third Witch:	Thou shalt get kings, though thou be none:
	So all hail, Macbeth and Banquo!
First Witch:	Banquo and Macbeth, all hail!
Macbeth:	Stay, you imperfect speakers, tell me more:

The extract on Sheet A is from a very famous play, 'Macbeth' by William Shakespeare.

The extract we have chosen comes from an early part of the play where Macbeth and Banquo are returning home from a battle and are crossing an area of open land. On this land there are three witches mixing a magic potion. The witches are able to predict the future. They are dancing around a cauldron, first in one direction and then in another, to help to get their potion ready.

Macbeth describes the day as 'foul' because the weather is so unpleasant but 'fair' because he has won a battle.

Banquo asks Macbeth how far it is to the town of Forres but before his companion can reply, he sees the witches and comments in amazement upon their appearances.

Macbeth commands the witches to speak. They hail him as the Lord of a place called Glamis. But they surprise him by praising him as Lord of Cawdor as well – this honour has been given by King Duncan but has not been announced to him yet. The witches know of it before Macbeth, purely by their magic. The greatest surprise of all is when the witches prophesy that Macbeth will be King!

Banquo wants to know his future. He asks the witches but their statements contain contradictions. Most importantly, they tell him that he will not be king but will be the father of kings.

© Andrew Brodie Publications ✓ PO Box 23, Wellington, Somerset, TA21 8YX ✓ www.andrewbrodie.co.uk

The extract from Macbeth contains some words, expressions and abbreviations that we would not use today. Match the expressions below with their modern versions. The first one is done for you.

thou	three times
thrice	you
is't	anything
on't	you
aught	you
thee	on it
doth	is it
ye	does

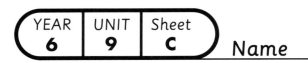

What are the three contradictory statements that the witches make about Banquo?

_____

_____

_____

_____

_____

Can you describe the three witches? There are lots of clues in the text to help you. Think about how they look but also what they say and do. Write your description below and continue in your exercise book if you need more space.

_____

_____

_____

_____

_____

_____

© Andrew Brodie Publications ✓ PO Box 23, Wellington, Somerset, TA21 8YX ✓ www.andrewbrodie.co.uk

Try to imagine that you are Macbeth or Banquo. Describe the meeting with the witches. If you choose to be Macbeth you could start like this:

The Strange Meeting

I was riding along with my good friend Banquo. The weather was terrible, windy and rainy, but we were in good spirits as we had just won a tremendous battle and were returning home. Imagine our surprise when we came across.....

_____

_____

_____

_____

_____

_____

_____

_____

_____

_____

_____

_____

_____

_____

_____

_____

_____

_____

_____

YEAR	UNIT	Sheet
6	10	A

Name   Strawberries

Strawberries

Sam couldn't quite make out if the strawberries were at their ripe, juicy readiness; that stage, when one bite sends the juices pouring down your chin, and the heavy sweetness fills your mouth. It was so much more difficult now to keep bending and checking. His old bones complained and creaked as he stooped to check the fruits. His eyesight wasn't what it had been, either, and he needed to be really close to see if they were quite ready to be plucked. He stood at the end of the scattered rows, in his allotment that he had tended for nearly fifty years now and ten years more before that, helping his old Da. He had loved those times together with his Dad, just the two of them, planting and tending, and finally the grand harvest. He had especially loved the time when the strawberries were ripe and a plump, ruby red, just ready for picking.

"This one's ready, Da. Look Da, this one is a beaut. Can I eat him now?"

"Hold on there, Sam, there won't be any left for tea if you carry on that way."
George loved to watch young Sam scamper about the allotment, and shared the lad's pleasure in the treasure that it provided. It was a real treasure too, when food was so scarce. The allotment had provided for the whole family, and many others were grateful for George's generous gifts of fruit and vegetables. Sam raced about at top speed but he never caught him putting a foot wrong. He never once trod on a straying lettuce, or knocked the towering bean sticks. He was a good lad.

Sam could see it all, now, playing like a film just before his eyes. He could see himself ten years old again, and not the seventy odd he really was. He still missed his old Da.

"Ah well," he said to himself, "those were grand days."

© Andrew Brodie Publications ✔ PO Box 23, Wellington, Somerset, TA21 8YX ✔ www.andrewbrodie.co.uk

A Slip in Time

"CD's. All the latest. Two for a fiver. You can't go wrong at that price"

How many times had I heard that? Anybody would think that all the sellers at this car boot sale were just giving their stuff away. I bet half of it was stolen, anyway. I was fed up trailing about after my Dad. We'd been at this car boot sale, that was at least the size of ten football pitches, for most of the day, and there looked like no chance of getting away before the next decade!

"Come on Sanjit," I hissed. "Let's go and have some real fun."

"What do you mean, Aaron?"

"Let's go and look at the stuff that we're interested in." I knew Sanjit was bored as well. He had only come along because his Dad had gone to work that day.

We slipped away and were quickly out of view of Dad and heading for the stalls with the computer games. I don't know what it was that made me stop at the doddery, old man's stall, stuffed full of dusty lampshades and weird statues, but something certainly halted me.

"What yer looking at that old thing for, Aaron? Come on let's get to the games." Sanjit was peering at the small statue I had in my hand.

I don't know how it happened, but suddenly I was handing over the money and buying the statue.

"Take great care, sonny," the old man muttered. "The statue is very special."

"What d'yer want that old thing for?" Sanjit grumbled.

"Dunno. I just like it."

As we threaded our way through the stalls, it seemed to me that at this side of the boot sale, people had dressed up in fancy dress. Why was it suddenly so hot? The sweat was pouring off me and the grass had apparently turned to sand. As I looked up, I realised that nothing was the same as it had been five minutes ago. Huge temples stood where there had only been blocks of flats. Sanjit seemed to be wearing a little dress thing and we were standing on the banks of a mighty river.

Donkeys were braying under their heavy burdens as they tramped along the dusty roads. As I watched, with amazement, I noticed a group of men heaving and straining to pull a huge stone, whilst others were shouting and hitting them to work harder. They were dragging it slowly on rollers towards a vast pyramid that was nearly half built.

"Which one do you like then?" enquired Sanjit. "This one's the latest. You have to shoot the purple monsters and collect the jewels."

"What are you talking about, Sanjit?" I stammered. " There are no computer games here. This must be Egypt, millions of years ago." But of course, there were the computer games, right in front of me and the car boot sale was all around me again.

© Andrew Brodie Publications ✓ PO Box 23, Wellington, Somerset, TA21 8YX ✓ www.andrewbrodie.co.uk

There are many ways in which stories can show the passing of time. In 'Strawberries', Sam has a 'flashback' to when he was a young boy. A 'flashback' tells us about a period in the past of a character's life.

1.   What evidence can you find to tell us that there is a 'flashback'?

_____

_____

2.   What do we learn about Sam as a young boy and Sam as an old man? Compare the two.

young Sam _____

_____

_____

_____

old Sam _____

_____

_____

_____

3.   The first paragraph in 'Strawberries' gives us basic details about Sam and describes his surroundings. It tells us a little of his childhood and something about his father.

Write a story plan to show how the story of 'Strawberries' might continue. Start by making short notes on the introduction that you have been given. Continue by making notes about a possible problem that might occur in the story. List some events that might take place. Finish with a solution to the problem or an interesting conclusion.

introduction _____

_____

_____

_____

problem _____

_____

_____

© Andrew Brodie Publications ✓ PO Box 23, Wellington, Somerset, TA21 8YX ✓ www.andrewbrodie.co.uk

events _____

_____

_____

_____

solution _____

_____

_____

_____

4. Work with a partner to make a list of phrases that can show the passing of time in a story. These phrases will often be used at the start of a paragraph and are useful to move the action of the story along.

Here are a few phrases to get you started. If you run out of ideas of your own, try looking in fiction books to find examples.

Later that night.......   **Next....**

It wasn't long before.....   **A few minutes later.....**

_____

_____

_____

_____

_____

_____

_____

_____

_____

_____

You could make a poster to put up in your classroom to remind everyone of these useful phrases.

5. Read the passage 'A Slip in Time'. This is the start of a story set in different time zones. In your exercise book, make a story plan to continue this story and then write the rest of the story. Be careful to show when the characters are moving from one time zone to another.

© Andrew Brodie Publications ✓ PO Box 23, Wellington, Somerset, TA21 8YX ✓ www.andrewbrodie.co.uk

This unit addresses the Literacy Strategy:
Term 2 objective   3: to recognise how poets manipulate words: - for their quality of sound, e.g. rhythm, rhyme, assonance; for the connotations;
                          - for multiple layers of meaning, e.g.. through figurative language, ambiguity.
Term 2 objective   4: to investigate humorous verse: - how poets play with meanings; - nonsense words and how meaning can be made of them;
                          - where the appeal lies.
Term 2 objective   5: to analyse how messages, moods, feelings and attitudes are conveyed in poetry.
Term 2 objective   6: to read and interpret poems in which meanings are implied or multi-layered,; to discuss, interpret challenging poems with
                          others.

Waves

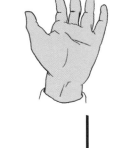

1.   Waves, at airports,
     On platforms,
     On driveways,
     Through windows.

2.   Waves, that carry
     Radio voices,
     TV pictures,
     Mobile messages.

3.   Waves, that roll
     Or tumble
     Or crash
     On distant shores.

4.   Waves, windswept,
     Twisting,
     Turning,
     Through tall grass.

5.   Waves, and curls,
     Or ringlets
     and quiffs
     On human heads.

6.   Waves, of heat
     In summer.
     Laziness
     On warm sands.

7.   Waves of feeling,
     Happiness,
     Sadness,
     In human hearts.

8.   Waves through windows
     That carry feeling
     To human hearts.
     And human heads.

© Andrew Brodie Publications ✓ PO Box 23, Wellington, Somerset, TA21 8YX ✓ www.andrewbrodie.co.uk

This poem explores various meanings of the word 'wave'.

Match the verse numbers to the meanings given below.
The first one is done for you.

1 —————————————————————————— undulating patterns made by the wind in grass

2   an expression describing hot weather

3   people gesticulating with their hands on parting or meeting

4   effect produced by the motion of water

5   changing emotions or moods

6   electronic signals

7   shapes made with hairstyles

Verse 8 combines ideas from three other verses. Which ones?

☐ ☐ ☐

Which verses imply that waves can carry messages?

☐ ☐ ☐

What do you think the writer meant by verse 8?
Give examples of waves and feelings that the writer could be referring to.

_____

_____

_____

_____

_____

_____

© Andrew Brodie Publications ✓ PO Box 23, Wellington, Somerset, TA21 8YX ✓ www.andrewbrodie.co.uk

Name _____

Waves

The word 'wave' is a homonym.
Using a dictionary to help you, identify different meanings for each of the homonyms given below.

sound _____

sound _____

sound _____

sound _____

roll _____

roll _____

roll _____

roll _____

fold _____

fold _____

fold _____

© Andrew Brodie Publications ✓ PO Box 23, Wellington, Somerset, TA21 8YX ✓ www.andrewbrodie.co.uk

fair _____

_____

fair _____

_____

fair _____

_____

fair _____

_____

ring _____

_____

ring _____

_____

ring _____

_____

Choose a homonym of your own, or one of those above, to create four simple verses of a poem. Then try to create a fifth verse that links some ideas from the others.

① _____

_____

_____

_____

③ _____

_____

_____

_____

② _____

_____

_____

④ _____

_____

_____

⑤ _____

_____

_____

_____

© Andrew Brodie Publications ✓ PO Box 23, Wellington, Somerset, TA21 8YX ✓ www.andrewbrodie.co.uk

This unit addresses the Literacy Strategy:
Term 2 objective   4: to investigate humourous verse: how poets play with meanings; nonsense words and how meanings can be made from them; where the appeal lies.

(1) THE TURTLE

The turtle is a funny bird,
It cannot fly, which is absurd.
Unless of course you turn the keys
And then it flies with soaring ease.
Twice round your head and soon it's gone,
To land on runway twenty-one.

(2) Joshua Lane

'I know I have lost my train'
Said a man named Joshua Lane;
'But I'll run on the rails
With my coat tails for sails
And maybe I'll catch it again.

Anon

(3) The Old Man of Blackheath

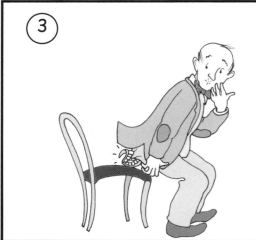

There was an old man of Blackheath
who sat on his set of false teeth
Said he, with a start,
'O, Lord, bless my heart!
I have bitten myself underneath!'

Anon

(4) My Dog

I've got a dog as thin as a rail,

He's got fleas all over his tail;

Every time his tail goes flop,

The fleas on the bottom all hop to the top.

Anon

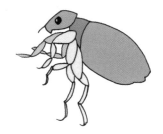

© Andrew Brodie Publications ✓ PO Box 23, Wellington, Somerset, TA21 8YX ✓ www.andrewbrodie.co.uk

1. Read the verse called 'The Turtle'. Make pictures, in your head, of the images in the poem. Write three separate scenes that the poem creates.

   1. _____

   _____

   2. _____

   _____

   3. _____

   _____

2. Do you find this poem amusing? Explain your answer.

   _____

   _____

   _____

   _____

3. Read the poem 'Joshua Lane' and draw the picture that it creates in your head.

4. 'The Old Man of Blackheath' is a particular type of humorous poem; it is called a limerick. Try writing your own limerick. Keep the length of lines and rhyming patterns the same as in the example.

   _____

   _____

   _____

   _____

   _____

5. Write out the poem 'My Dog', in your best handwriting on the back of this sheet. Think of different words to replace the words 'rail' and 'top' in the poem. Try to replace them with words that will still make the poem funny.

© Andrew Brodie Publications ✓ PO Box 23, Wellington, Somerset, TA21 8YX ✓ www.andrewbrodie.co.uk

Try to write about four lines of amusing verse yourself and draw a cartoon picture to illustrate it.

Verse	Picture

Nonsense words.

I scrumble by the floply scube
And drindoll balong the droob.
Gruda jowted all the nem,
So I boluby groob.

This verse is complete nonsense but we can still work out what place the nonsense word would take in the sentence. For example:

I scrumble by the floply scube.

verb   adjective   noun

Can you find 2 more nonsense nouns and 2 more nonsense verbs?
Think about the endings of verbs (e.g. ed, ing) and this will help you.

Nonsense verbs	Nonsense nouns

© Andrew Brodie Publications ✓ PO Box 23, Wellington, Somerset, TA21 8YX ✓ www.andrewbrodie.co.uk

Write some four-line nonsense verses on your own or with a partner.
It will help you if you write four lines that make sense and then substitute in some nonsense
words with appropriate endings for verbs and adjectives. Nouns have no particular endings.

e.g.

    sense   - **I walked along the golden sand.**
    nonsense   - **I gloffed beerong the drofen crov.**

This unit addresses the Literacy Strategy:
Term 1 objective   4: to be familiar with the work of some established authors, to know what is special about their work, and to explain their preferences in terms of authors, styles and themes.
Term 2 objective   4: to investigate humourous verse: how poets play with meanings; nonsense words and how meaning can be made of them; where the appeal lies.
Term 2 objective   9: to increase the familiarity with significant poets and writers of the past.

Name   Nonsense Poems

The two poems on these pages are both by the author Lewis Carroll who lived from 1832 to 1898. He wrote many well-known poems as well as the stories of Alice's Adventures in Wonderland and Alice through the Looking Glass.

Did you know that 'Lewis Carroll' was the author's 'pen name'?

His real name was Charles Dodgson.

1 'Twas brillig, and the slithy toves
        Did gyre and gimble in the wabe;
   All mimsy were the borogroves,
        And the mome raths outgrabe.

2 'Beware the Jabberwock, my son!
        The jaws that bite, the claws that catch!
   Beware the Jubjub bird and shun
        The frumious Bandersnatch!'

3 He took his vorpal sword in hand:
        Long time the manxome foe he sought -
   So rested he by the Tumtum tree,
        And stood awhile in thought.

4 And as in uffish thought he stood,
        The Jabberwock, with eyes of flame,
   Came whiffling through the tulgey wood,
        And burbled as it came!

5 One, two! One, two! And through and through,
        The vorpal blade went snicker-snack!
   He left it dead, and with its head
        He went galumphing back.

6 'And hast thou slain the Jabberwock?
        Come to my arms, my beamish boy!
   O frabjous day! Callooh! Callay!'
        He chortled in his joy.

7 'Twas brillig, and the slithy toves
        Did gyre and gimble in the wabe;
   All mimsy were the borogroves,
        And the mome raths outgrabe.

© Andrew Brodie Publications ✔ PO Box 23, Wellington, Somerset, TA21 8YX ✔ www.andrewbrodie.co.uk

SOME HALLUCINATIONS

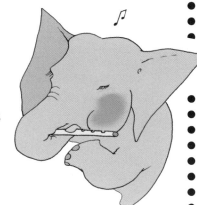

He thought he saw an Elephant,
That practised on a fife:
He looked again, and found it was
A letter from his wife.
'At length I realize,' he said,
'The bitterness of Life!'

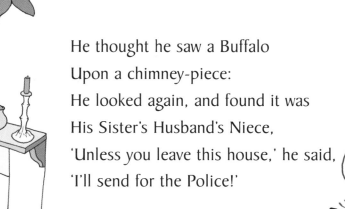

He thought he saw a Buffalo
Upon a chimney-piece:
He looked again, and found it was
His Sister's Husband's Niece,
'Unless you leave this house,' he said,
'I'll send for the Police!'

He thought he saw a Rattlesnake
That questioned him in Greek:
He looked again, and found it was
The Middle of Next Week.
'The one thing I regret,' he said,
'Is that it cannot speak!'

He thought he saw a Banker's Clerk
Descending from the bus:
He looked again, and found it was
A Hippopotamus:
'If this should stay to dinner,' he said,
'There won't be much for us!'

© Andrew Brodie Publications ✓ PO Box 23, Wellington, Somerset, TA21 8YX ✓ www.andrewbrodie.co.uk

Basic Comprehension

Both of the poems you have just read are 'Nonsense Poems' by Lewis Carroll.

1. Which poem uses nonsense words?

    _____

2. Which poem uses impossible ideas?

    _____

3. Write the first 4 invented words found in the 'Jabberwocky' poem.

4. Write the last 4 invented words found in the same poem.

5. Use the boxes to draw pictures that you think illustrate the 1st verse of each poem.

SOME HALLUCINATIONS   JABBERWOCKY

More Advanced Comprehension

When you have completed this work, find out all you can about the works of Lewis Carroll.

6.　Here are some of the nonsense words from Jabberwocky. Next to each word, write a real word that you think could be nearest to its meaning.

brillig _____　**manxome** _____

frumious _____　**frabjous** _____

uffish _____　**galumphing** _____

7.　In your own words explain how the final verse of 'Some Hallucinations' develops the humour of the poem.

_____

_____

_____

_____

_____

8.　Which of the poems do you prefer?
Give reasons for your answer.

_____

_____

_____

_____

_____

Either:
　　Choose a verse of 'Jabberwocky' to 'translate' into what you think the 'real English' version might be. (Don't worry about rhythm or rhyme, the meaning is the important thing.)

　　or

　　Try to write an additional verse to the poem 'Some Hallucinations'.

© Andrew Brodie Publications ✓ PO Box 23, Wellington, Somerset, TA21 8YX ✓ www.andrewbrodie.co.uk

This unit addresses the Literacy Strategy:
Term 2 objective   5: to analyse how messages, moods, feelings and attitudes are conveyed in poetry.
Term 2 objective   9: to increase familiarity with significant poets and writers of the past.
Term 3 objective   4: to comment critically on the overall impact of a poem, showing how language and themes have been developed.
Term 3 objective   5: to compare and contrast the work of a single writer.

Emily Brontë (1818-1848)

Emily Brontë and her two sisters, Charlotte and Anne, are all famous for their stories and poetry.

Emily was born in Yorkshire on July 30th 1818. Her father was a parson of the church at Haworth, a village on the Yorkshire Moors. The family lived in the Parsonage, close to the church.

Emily and her sisters had wonderful imaginations. They made up stories with their wooden toys and set them in imaginary kingdoms called Angria and Gondal. Many of their handwritten volumes of these stories still survive today.

There were sad times in Emily's childhood; her mother died in 1824 when Emily was only 6 and she was sent to boarding school with Charlotte and their two older sisters, Maria and Elizabeth. Maria and Elizabeth both became ill at the school and died (in 1825). Charlotte and Emily were taken away from the school because of the grim conditions there.

Emily wrote many poems which she kept hidden until they were discovered by Charlotte who thought they should be published.
In 1847 Emily's most famous novel, 'Wuthering Heights' was published. A year later she died at only 30 years of age.

Emily Brontë's writing was influenced by the bleak landscape of the Yorkshire Moors and the cold damp conditions she experienced during the winters at Haworth.

These are two of Emily Brontë's poems. The second is untitled.

SPELLBOUND

The night is darkening round me,
The wild winds coldly blow;
But a tyrant spell has bound me
And I cannot, cannot go.

The giant trees are bending
Their bare boughs weighed with snow.
The storm is fast descending,
And yet I cannot go.

Clouds beyond clouds above me,
Wastes beyond wastes below;
But nothing drear can move me;
I will not, cannot go.

Heavy hangs the raindrops
From the burdened spray;
Heavy broods the damp mist
On Uplands far away;

Heavy looms the dull sky.
Heavy rolls the sea —
And heavy beats the young heart
Beneath that lonely tree -

© Andrew Brodie Publications ✓ PO Box 23, Wellington, Somerset, TA21 8YX ✓ www.andrewbrodie.co.uk

> **You will need to refer to the information on Emily Bronte to ¨answer these questions.**

1. Emily Bronte had four sisters altogether.
   Name the two sisters who are also famous for their writing.

   ① _____ ② _____

2. Name the county where Emily lived.   _____

3. Name the two imaginary kingdoms where Emily and her sisters set their stories when they were children.

   ① _____ ② _____

4. According to the text, what influenced Emily's writing?

   _____
   _____
   _____
   _____

> **You will need to read the two poems by Emily Bronte to answër these questions.**

1. Circle two words which you think best describe the mood of the poet in the poem titled Spellbound.

   (**happy**) (**gloomy**) (**scared**) (**cheerful**)

© Andrew Brodie Publications ✓ PO Box 23, Wellington, Somerset, TA21 8YX ✓ www.andrewbrodie.co.uk

2. In the second poem the poet used the word 'heavy' five times. How does this help to set the mood of the poem and tell us how the poet was feeling?

_____

_____

_____

_____

3. How do the poet's references to the landscape and weather conditions set the mood of the poem?

_____

_____

_____

_____

4. Write a poem which makes references to the landscape to set the mood you want to convey.

Some suggestions for first lines:
a. *The shimmering sea reflects the golden glory of the sun......*
b. *The bare trees in silhouette against the blackened sky......*
c. *Tears of rain are running down the window pane.*

_____

_____

_____

_____

_____

_____

_____

_____

_____

This unit addresses the Literacy Strategy:
Term 1 objective   4: to be familiar with the work of some established authors, to know what is special about their work, and to explain their preferences in terms of authors, styles and themes.
Term 1 objective   5: to contribute constructively to shared discussion about literature, responding to and building on the views of others.
②Term 2 objective   3: to recognise how poets manipulate words - for their quality of sound, e.g. rhythm, rhyme, assonance - for the connotations - for multiple layers of meaning, e.g. through figurative language, ambiguity.
Term 2 objective   5: to analyse how messages, moods, feelings and attitudes are conveyed in poetry.
Term 2 objective   6: to read and interpret poems in which meanings are implied or multi-layered; to discuss, interpret challenging poems with others.
Term 3 objective   3: to describe and evaluate the style of an individual poet.
Term 3 objective   4: to comment critically on the overall impact of a poem, showing how language and themes have been developed.

YEAR **6** | UNIT **15** | Sheet **A**   Name   Four Great Poets

Four Great Poets of the Past

Most people have heard of many of the great poets of the past, but may be unfamiliar with much of their work. On these two pages we will be looking at samples of the work of just four great poets, William Shakespeare, Robert Burns, Christina Rossetti and William Wordsworth. All the poems referred to in this text are more than a hundred years old, but the magic of the words lives on today. Some of the oldest poems may be less easy to understand, but if this is the case, then reading the words aloud and with appropriate expression may help.

Perhaps the most famous of all our poets was the great poet and playwright **William Shakespeare** who lived from 1564 to 1616. Amongst other things he wrote more than one hundred and fifty sonnets. A sonnet is a 14 line verse written in ① **iambic pentameter**, and is usually split into 8 lines then 6 lines. One famous sonnet by Shakespeare, begins...

Shall I compare thee to a Summer's day?
Thou art more lovely and more temperate:
Rough Windes do shake the darling buds of Maie,
And Sommers lease hath all too short a date:

In this sonnet a loved one is being compared to a summer's day. It is interesting to note some of the old forms of spelling seen in some of the words.

Another famous poet of the past is the Scottish poet **Robert Burns**, who lived from 1759 to 1796. You may be aware of the Burns' Night celebrations in Scotland each year on January 25th (the poet's birthday) when his work is celebrated. Burns' poems are written in the Scottish dialect which makes them interesting both to read aloud and to listen to. Here is the first verse of a well known poem by Robert Burns.②

Ye banks and braes and streams around
    The castle o'Montgomery,
Green be your woods, and fair your flowers,
    Your waters never drumlie!
There simmer first unfauld her robes,
    And there the langest tarry;
For there I took the last fareweel
    O'my sweet Highland Mary.

---

① Iambic Pentameter is poetry made of regular lines. Each line has pairs of syllables in which the 1st is short and the 2nd is long. (E.g. di dah, di dah)
②Another poem by Robert Burns (To a Mouse) can be found in Writing for Literacy for ages 9-10. Also published by Andrew Brodie Publications.

© Andrew Brodie Publications ✓ PO Box 23, Wellington, Somerset, TA21 8YX ✓ www.andrewbrodie.co.uk

Another great poet of the past is **Christina Rossetti** who lived from 1830 to 1894. She wrote poetry for both adults and children. You may have already encountered a number of her poems.①

This poem is one of her best known.

Remember me when I am gone away,
　　Gone far away into the silent land;
　　When you can no more hold me by the hand,
Not I half turn to go yet turning stay.
Remember me when no more day by day
　　You tell me of our future that you planned:
　　Only remember me; you understand
It will be late to counsel then or pray.
Yet if you should forget me for a while
　　And afterwards remember, do not grieve:
　　For if the darkness and corruption leave
A vestige of the thoughts that once I had,
Better by far you should forget and smile
　　Than that you should remember and be sad.

The last of the four poets we are thinking about today is **William Wordsworth** who lived from 1770 to 1850. Perhaps the best known of his poems is 'The Daffodils'. Most people know the first verse of this famous work. There are another three verses to this poem, and you can find it in most good anthologies.②

Not all Wordsworth's poems were about the countryside. This poem is about the city of London:

I wander'd lonely as a cloud
That floats on high o'er vales and hills,
When all at once I saw a crowd,
A host of golden daffodils,
Beside the lake, beneath the trees
Fluttering and dancing in the breeze.

Upon Westminster Bridge - Sept 3. 1802

Earth has not anything to show more fair:
Dull would he be of soul who could pass by
A sight so touching in its majesty:
This City now doth like a garment wear
The beauty of the morning: silent, bare,
Ships, towers, domes, theatres, and temples lie
Open unto the fields, and to the sky,
All bright and glittering in the smokeless air.
Never did sun more beautifully steep
In his first splendour, valley, rock, or hill;
Ne'er saw I, never felt, a calm so deep!
The river glideth at his own sweet will:
Dear God! the very houses seem asleep;
And all that mighty heart is lying still!

① Four of her poems for younger readers can be found in Writing for Literacy for ages 9-10 (Andrew Brodie Publications).
②An anthology is a collection of poems by various authors.

© Andrew Brodie Publications ✓ PO Box 23, Wellington, Somerset, TA21 8YX ✓ www.andrewbrodie.co.uk

Basic Comprehension

1. Name the four poets referred to in the text, and the years of their births and deaths.

    _____   _____   _____

    _____   _____   _____

    _____   _____   _____

    _____   _____   _____

2. Which of the poems is about death? Give reasons for your answer.

    _____

    _____

    _____

    _____

3. Which of the poets was born in Scotland?   _____

4. What special feature of his poetry makes his work interesting to read and listen to?

    _____

    _____

    _____

5. Which of the poets is famous for writing plays?

    _____

6. In the extract from the poem by William Shakespeare, some words are spelt in an old way. Write the modern spelling beside each one below.

    windes _____   **hath** _____

    Maie _____   **sommer** _____

7. The extract from the sonnet is just four lines long.
    How long is a complete sonnet?   _____

8. Name two poems written by William Wordsworth.

    _____

    _____

© Andrew Brodie Publications ✓ PO Box 23, Wellington, Somerset, TA21 8YX ✓ www.andrewbrodie.co.uk

9. With a partner (or in a small group) investigate other poems written by one or more of the four poets. List the poems by title and author on the back of this sheet. Write the poem you like best, from those you have found, in your best handwriting. You may illustrate it if you wish to.

10. What is **iambic pentameter**?

_____

_____

11. Name two places you might look to find more poems by Christina Rossetti.

_____

_____

12. Explain any details you have noticed about the structure of the poem 'Upon Westminster Bridge' by William Wordsworth.

_____

_____

_____

13. Read the first verse of 'Highland Mary'.
In one sentence, explain what you think the poem is about.

_____

_____

14. There is a simile in the first verse of each of the poems by William Wordsworth. Write them both below.

_____

_____

15. Which of the extracts do you like best? Give reasons for your answer.

_____

_____

_____

Group Work - make an anthology.
Each member of the group should choose a famous poet of the past (there are many to choose from) and write out their two favourite poems by that poet.
These should be combined to make a group anthology. With your presentation of each poem you must write a reason for your choice.

© Andrew Brodie Publications ✓ PO Box 23, Wellington, Somerset, TA21 8YX ✓ www.andrewbrodie.co.uk

This unit addresses the Literacy Strategy:
Term 2 objective 15: to recognise how arguments are constructed to be effective, through, e.g. the expression, sequence and linking of points; the provision of persuasive examples, illustrations and evidence; pre-empting or answering potential objections; appealing to the known views and feelings of the audience.
Term 2 objective 16: to identify the features of balanced written arguments with e.g. summarise different sides of an argument; clarify the strengths and weaknesses of different positions; signal personal opinion clearly.

35 Juniper Crescent
Langbourne
Chetminster
Somerset
TA2 6PQ
21st June 2002

Dear Sir,

My partner and I visited your restaurant last week, for an evening meal. When we arrived, we were delighted to see that the room was beautifully laid out, with candles and flowers at each table, and we looked forward with anticipation to excellent food and a pleasant evening. The food was indeed excellent and the chef must be congratulated on his very varied menu. However, I was extremely concerned when a gentleman at the table next to ours lit a cigarette at the end of his meal. I was amazed to find, in this enlightened age, that smoking is still allowed in some restaurants. I find this a disgusting and deplorable act and am truly amazed to find that you allow such behaviour to take place, in your otherwise excellent restaurant.

Surely you must realise the unpleasant consequences of allowing people to smoke in an eating area. Many people are made physically sick by the smell of tobacco, or at the least it makes them cough. My partner is slightly asthmatic and the 'fug' created by the smoke in your restaurant made him very tight-chested the next day. I do not wish to be in an environment where I am forced to inhale other people's exhaled smoke. It is a fact that smoking causes cancer, and there is evidence to show that even being in a smoky room can put your health at risk. I really do not see how you can encourage smoking in a place where good tasty food is served, when it is an established fact that smoking damages your sense of taste. Surely you want your customers to taste their food. The smell of the smoke lingered with us, and the next day I could still smell it on my hair and clothes. I am sure there are a few people who enjoy smoking, but surely they could be persuaded to step outside to smoke, or just not have a cigarette for a few hours.

I would sincerely urge you to consider a change in your attitude to smoking in your restaurant. In my opinion, you are losing many customers by allowing smoking in your restaurant. I hope to be able to visit your restaurant again sometime in the future when you have reconsidered your smoking policy.

Yours faithfully

B Vinny

Barbara Vinny

© Andrew Brodie Publications ✓ PO Box 23, Wellington, Somerset, TA21 8YX ✓ www.andrewbrodie.co.uk

Name **Smoking**

> An **argument** is a persuasive piece of writing from one point of view.
> A **discussion** gives a balanced argument from different view points.

1. Is the letter to the restaurant a discussion or an argument?

   _____

> When you write an argument, you are trying
> to persuade somebody to do something.

2. Who is the letter trying to persuade?

   _____

3. What is the writer trying to persuade them to do?

   _____

   _____

   _____

4. Read the letter carefully and find examples of persuasive language.
   The first one in paragraphs 1 and 2 are done for you,.

   Paragraph 1

   1. **However, I was extremely concerned...**

   2. _____

   3. _____

   Paragraph 2

   1. **Surely you must realise...**

   2. _____

   3. _____

   Paragraph 3

   1. _____

© Andrew Brodie Publications ✓ PO Box 23, Wellington, Somerset, TA21 8YX ✓ www.andrewbrodie.co.uk

Name _____   Smoking

The letter is split into 3 paragraphs.

Ist paragraph   -   An introduction and background to the problem.
2nd paragraph   -   The arguments against smoking in the restaurant.
3rd paragraph   -   The writer's personal opinions and conclusions.

5.   Write brief notes about the main ideas included in each paragraph.

1st _____

_____

2nd _____

_____

3rd _____

_____

6.   Why do you think this letter writer said that she was sure that there were people who enjoyed smoking?

_____

_____

_____

7.   What do you think a 'fug' is like? Describe it in a few sentences.

_____

_____

_____

_____

8.   What did the writer mean by 'enlightened age'?

_____

_____

9.   Use a dictionary to find the meanings of these words from the text.

inhale _____

exhale _____

anticipation _____

consequences _____

lingered _____

© Andrew Brodie Publications ✓ PO Box 23, Wellington, Somerset, TA21 8YX ✓ www.andrewbrodie.co.uk

10.   Here are some arguments that people have said, both for and
      against smoking. Write the corresponding letters in the correct columns.

A   'It makes the room smell.'

B   'I can't breathe when I am near someone who smokes.'

C   'It clears my head and makes me think clearly.'

D   'It's a habit. I can't stop. I get very irritable if I try to give up.'

E   'Being in a smoky room makes me cough.'

F   'It adds to air pollution.'

G   'The government uses the tax money collected from cigarettes to
      help other people.'

H   'It costs the country millions of pounds giving smokers health care.'

I   'Smoking gives you lung cancer.'

J   'If people don't like us smoking, then they can go somewhere else.'

K   'Breathing in other people's old smoke can make you ill.'

Arguments for	Arguments against

11.   Use the back of the sheet to write a balanced discussion about smoking.
      Your first paragraph should be an introduction to the topic. You should
      then discuss the arguments, both for and against smoking. Finally you
      can give you own opinion saying why you hold this opinion.
      These phrases may help you:-

There is evidence that.... Some people believe...   However...

They also argue that.....   On the other hand.....   In my opinion...

Others think...   It is a fact that.....

© Andrew Brodie Publications ✓ PO Box 23, Wellington, Somerset, TA21 8YX ✓ www.andrewbrodie.co.uk

YEAR	UNIT	Sheet
6	17	A

Name

Reading the Small Print

On these two pages you will see examples of holiday insurance policies.

Read them carefully, they are not as straightforward as they seem.

SUNNY DAYS HOLIDAY INSURANCE

<u>Summary of Insurance Cover</u> for one holiday not exceeding 21 days.

	Description of Item	Amount of Cover (Per person)
1.	Holiday cancellation/curtailment	Full cost of holiday
2.	Medical Expenses	Up to £250,000
3.	Baggage loss	Up to £1,000
4.	Delayed baggage	Up to £100
5.	Money loss	Up to £500
6.	Delayed travel	£25 for first 12 hours £20 for each additional 6 hours (up to a maximum of £150)
7.	Hijack	£10 per day up to maximum of £200
8.	Missed Departure	Up to £500
9.	Personal Accident - loss of limb	£5,000
	- loss of sight	£5,000
	- Total disablement	£20,000
	- Death Benefit	£10,000

Notes.

❐ All claims must be made in writing within 7 days of incident or return from holiday - whichever is the sooner.

❐ No claims can be made in case of war or major natural disaster.

❐ Sections 3,6,7,8, and 9 are subject to an excess payment of £50 per claim.

❐ Hijacks (section 7) in excess of ten days are not covered by this policy.

❐ Insured people must take all reasonable precautions to avoid accident, loss or illness.

❐ Thefts must be reported to the local police within 24 hours.

❐ This insurance does not cover people participating in the following hazardous activities: rock climbing, abseiling, scuba diving, parachute jumping, skiing, water skiing, motor-racing.

❐ Claims made for holiday cancellation or curtailment (section1).
These will only be to cover cancellation in the case of serious illness of a) the insured b) a close relative of the insured c) a travelling companion of the insured.

❐ This insurance is valid only in Great Britain, Europe and Australasia.

© Andrew Brodie Publications ✓ PO Box 23, Wellington, Somerset, TA21 8YX ✓ www.andrewbrodie.co.uk

Advanced Comprehension

☂ In the notes of both the insurance policies 'excess' payments are referred to. What does this mean?

_____

_____

_____

☂ If, when covered by a 'Sunny Days' insurance policy, your baggage worth £550 is lost, will the insurance company pay you the whole £550? Explain your answer.

_____

_____

_____

☂ A man aged 75 is going to Germany for a two week holiday. Which insurance policy should he choose? Explain your answer.

_____

_____

_____

☂ Which is the better policy to choose for a tourist who wants to go scuba diving? Explain your answer.

_____

_____

_____

☂ Which policy is better for a tourist going to Australia for 24 days? Explain your answer.

_____

_____

_____

☂ If you decide not to go on holiday as you are very worried about your seriously ill dog, can you claim on your insurance policy? Explain your answer.

_____

_____

_____

© Andrew Brodie Publications ✓ PO Box 23, Wellington, Somerset, TA21 8YX ✓ www.andrewbrodie.co.uk

This unit addresses the Literacy Strategy:
Term 1 objective   4: to be familiar with the work of some established authors, to know what is special about their work, and to explain their preferences in terms of authors, styles and themes.
Term 2 objective   3: to recognise how poets manipulate words: for their quality of sound, e.g. rhythm, rhyme, assonance; for the connotations; for multiple layers of meaning, e.g. through figurative language, ambiguity.
Term 2 objective   5: to analyse how messages, moods, feelings and attitudes are conveyed in poetry.
Term 3 objective   2: to discuss how linked poems relate to one another by themes, format and repetition, e.g. cycle of poems about the seasons.
Term 3 objective   4: to comment critically on the overall impact of a poem, showing how language and themes have been developed.

| YEAR 6 | UNIT 18 | Sheet A |

Name   Moon Poems

These three poems, though quite different from one another, are linked by the theme of the moon. They are all by very well-known poets.

Can you find any other poems about the moon?

SILVER
By Walter De La Mare 1873-1956

Slowly, silently, now the moon

Walks the night in her silver shoon;

     This way, and that, she peers, and sees

     Silver fruit upon silver trees;

     One by one the casements catch

     Her beams beneath the silvery thatch;

   Couched in his kennel, like a log,

With paws of silver sleeps the dog;

From their shadowy cote the white breasts peep

Of doves in a silver-feathered sleep;

A harvest mouse goes scampering by,

With silver claws, and silver eye;

And moveless fish in the water gleam,

By silver reeds in a silver stream.

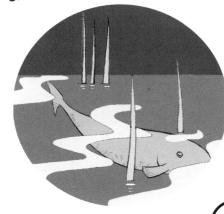

Reproduced by kind permission of The Literary Trustees of Walter de la Mare and the Society of Authors as their representative.

© Andrew Brodie Publications ✓ PO Box 23, Wellington, Somerset, TA21 8YX ✓ www.andrewbrodie.co.uk

Lady Moon
by Christina Rossetti 1830 - 1894

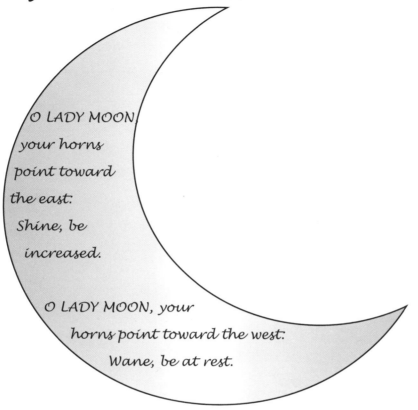

O LADY MOON,
your horns
point toward
the east:
Shine, be
increased.

O LADY MOON, your
horns point toward the west:
Wane, be at rest.

THE MOON
By Robert Louis Stevenson 1850-1894

The moon has a face like the clock in the hall;
She shines on thieves on the garden wall,
On streets and fields and harbour quays,
And birdies asleep in the forks of the trees.

The squalling cat and the squeaking mouse,
The howling dog by the door of the house,
The bat that lies in bed at noon,
All love to be out by the light of the moon.

But all of the things that belong to the day
Cuddle to sleep to be out of her way;
And flowers and children close their eyes
Till up in the morning the sun shall rise.

Comprehension

○ In the poem 'Silver', name the word used by the poet instead of 'shoes' and explain why you think he did this.

_____

_____

_____

○ Which of the poems do you think was written for younger children?

_____

○ Which poem could be used to help you to remember the way the moon waxes and wanes? What do 'waxing' and 'waning' mean?

_____

_____

_____

○ In the poem 'Silver' which word is used instead of 'windows'?

_____

○ In the first verse of 'The Moon' which word do you think is a particularly childish one?

_____

○ In the poem 'Silver', how many times is the word 'silver' used and why do you think the poet has done this?

_____

_____

_____

○ In two clear sentences say which of the poems you liked best, and give reasons for your choice.

_____

_____

_____

© Andrew Brodie Publications ✓ PO Box 23, Wellington, Somerset, TA21 8YX ✓ www.andrewbrodie.co.uk

Advanced Comprehension

○ What gender is attributed to the moon in all three poems?

_____

○ Why do you think the poets chose to do this?

_____

_____

○ On the lines below write two examples of similes to be found in the poems.

_____

_____

○ Use the lines below to write 2 examples of metaphorical language in the poems.

_____

_____

_____

○ In addition to the subject matter, what do these three poems have in common? (Look at the way the poems are constructed to answer this.)

_____

_____

○ In the poem 'Silver', what do you imagine the weather to be like?

_____

_____

○ How do you think the poet makes you think this?

_____

_____

_____

Create a 'moon' poem of your own.
You may choose to use rhyming couplets.

○ ○ ○

Investigate other poems by one of the 3 poets.

© Andrew Brodie Publications ✓ PO Box 23, Wellington, Somerset, TA21 8YX ✓ www.andrewbrodie.co.uk

This unit addresses the Literacy Strategy:
Term 2 objective   3: to recognise how poets manipulate words; for their quality of sound, e.g. rhythm, rhyme, assonance; for the connotations;
                        for multiple layers of meaning, e.g.. through figurative language, ambiguity.
Term 2 objective   5: to analyse how messages, moods, feelings and attitudes are conveyed in poetry.
Term 2 objective   9: to increase familiarity with significant poets and writers of the past.
Term 3 objective   3: to describe and evaluate the style of an individual poet.
Term 3 objective   6: to look at connections and contrasts in the work of different writers.

'SNAKE' D H Lawrence

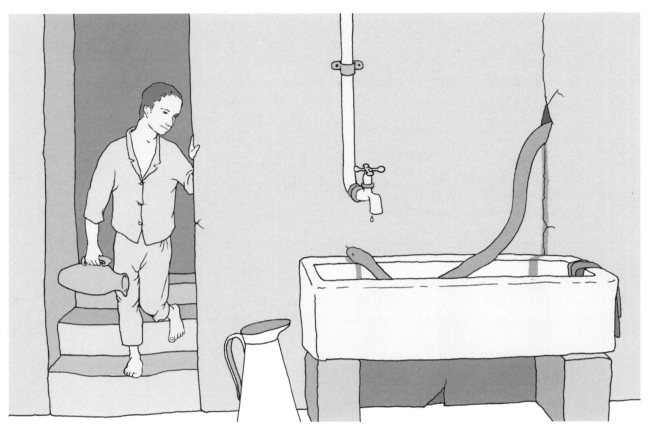

Extract from 'Snake' by D H Lawrence. Reproduced by kind permission of Pollinger Ltd and the Estate of Frieda Lawrence Ravagli.

A snake came to my water-trough
On a hot, hot day, and I in pyjamas for the heat,
To drink there.

In the deep, strange-scented shade of the great dark carob-tree
5 I came down the steps with my pitcher
And must wait, must stand and wait, for there he was at the trough before me.

He reached down from a fissure in the earth-wall in the gloom
And trailed his yellow-brown slackness soft-bellied down, over the edge of the stone
trough
10 And rested his throat upon the stone bottom,
And where the water had dripped from the tap, in a small clearness,
He sipped with his straight mouth,
Softly drank through his straight gums, into his slack long body,
Silently.

15 Someone was before me at my water-trough,
And I, like a second comer, waiting.

Extract from 'Snake' by D H Lawrence. Reproduced by kind permission of Pollinger Ltd and the Estate of Frieda Lawrence Ravagli.

He lifted his head from his drinking, as cattle do,
And looked at me vaguely, as drinking cattle do,
And flickered his two-forked tongue from his lips, and mused a moment,
20 And stooped and drank a little more,
Being earth-brown, earth-golden from the burning bowels of the earth
On the day of Sicilian July, with Etna smoking.

The voice of my education said to me
He must be killed,
25 For in Sicily the black, black snakes are innocent, the gold are venomous.

And voices in me said, If you were a man
You would take a stick and break him now, and finish him off.

But must I confess how I liked him,
How glad I was he had come like a guest in quiet, to drink at my water-trough
30 And depart peaceful, pacified, and thankless,
Into the burning bowels of this earth?

Was it cowardice, that I dared not kill him?
Was it perversity, that I longed to talk to him?
Was it humility, to feel so honoured?
35 I felt so honoured.

D H Lawrence

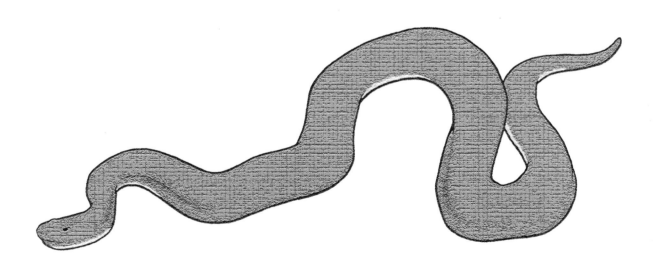

© Andrew Brodie Publications ✓ PO Box 23, Wellington, Somerset, TA21 8YX ✓ www.andrewbrodie.co.uk

For this section you will need to read the extract from the poem called 'Snake' by D.H.Lawrence.

Put a ring around the word or group of words which answers the question most accurately.

1. Who is the narrator in the poem called 'Snake'?

   (**the poet**)   (**the snake**)   (**someone else**)

2. What was the narrator about to do when he saw the snake?

   (**go for a walk**)   (**go to bed**)   (**get some water**)

3. Find two lines that tell us that the narrator liked the snake.

   1. _____

   _____

   2. _____

   _____

4. Was the snake poisonous? How do you know?

   _____

   _____

   _____

5. The poem is numbered every five lines. E.g. Line 15 starts with the word 'someone'. Find the word at the start of each of these lines:

   12 [   ]   3 [   ]   31 [   ]

   20 [   ]   29 [   ]   8 [   ]

6. Find the line number for each of these starts:

   Softly ... [   ]   **How glad ...** [   ]   **He sipped ...** [   ]

   For in ... [   ]   **And voices ...** [   ]   **I felt ...** [   ]

© Andrew Brodie Publications ✓ PO Box 23, Wellington, Somerset, TA21 8YX ✓ www.andrewbrodie.co.uk

7. Read lines 12, 13 and 14 of the poem;

'He sipped with his straight mouth,
softly drank through his straight gums, into his slack long body,
Silently.'

What effect do you think the poet was trying to achieve by using the letter 's' at the start of so many words in these lines?

_____

_____

_____

_____

_____

8. There is a special name for repeating the same letter at the start of words. What is this special name?

9. On seeing the snake the poet reacted quite differently to the narrator in the extract from 'The Green Mamba' in Unit 5. Complete the sentence below to explain the mood of the poet on seeing the snake.

On seeing the snake the poet felt... _____

_____

_____

_____

10. In lines 17 and 18 D H Lawrence compares the snake to cattle. Why is this so effective?

_____

_____

_____

_____

_____

_____

© Andrew Brodie Publications ✓ PO Box 23, Wellington, Somerset, TA21 8YX ✓ www.andrewbrodie.co.uk

Comparing and contrasting 'The Green Mamba' extract by R Dahl and 'Snake' by D H Lawrence.

8. Compare the different ways that the authors reacted when they came upon a snake. Use words or extracts from the texts to illustrate your answer.

_____

_____

_____

_____

_____

_____

_____

_____

_____

_____

_____

_____

_____

_____

_____

_____

Work on the back of the sheet if you run out of space.

9. In the poem 'Snake' the poet uses both long and short lines. How does this affect the pace of the story told in the poem? How does this compare with the extract from 'The Green Mamba'?

_____

_____

_____

_____

_____

_____

_____

_____

Work on the back of the sheet if you run out of space.

© Andrew Brodie Publications ✓ PO Box 23, Wellington, Somerset, TA21 8YX ✓ www.andrewbrodie.co.uk

Continuing the story or poem

What happens next?

Choose either 'The Green Mamba' or 'Snake' and write what <u>you</u> think could happen next. If you would like to know what really happened in Roald Dahl's true story, this can be read in his book 'Going Solo'.

_____

_____

_____

_____

_____

_____

_____

_____

_____

_____

_____

_____

_____

_____

_____

_____

_____

_____

_____

_____

_____

_____

_____

_____

This unit addresses the Literacy Strategy:
Term 3 objective   6: to took at connections and contrasts in the work of different writers.

YEAR **6** | UNIT **20** | Sheet **A**   **Name**   **Comparing Texts**

Stig of the Dump by Clive King

It seemed to be partly a cave dug into the chalk, partly a shelter built out over the mouth of the cave. There was a cool, damp smell. Woodlice and earwigs dropped from the roof where he had broken through it …

… He'd never seen anything like the collection of bits and pieces, odds and ends, bric-a-brac and old brock, that this Stig creature had lying about his den. There were stones and bones, fossils and bottles, skins and tins, stacks of sticks and hanks of string. There were motor-car tyres and hats from old scarecrows, nuts and bolts and bobbles from brass bedsteads. There was a coal scuttle full of old electric light bulbs and a basin with rusty screws and nails in it. There was a pile of bracken and newspapers that looked as if it had never been given a tidy-up.

"I wish I lived here," said Barney.

Stig seemed to understand that Barney was approving of his home and his face lit up. He took on the air of a householder showing a visitor round his property, and began pointing out some things that he seemed particularly proud of.

First, the plumbing. Where the water dripped through a crack in the roof of the cave he had wedged the mud-guard of a bicycle. The water ran along this, through the tube of a vacuum-cleaner, and into a big can with writing on it. By the side of this was a plastic football carefully cut in half, and Stig dipped up some water and offered it to Barney. Barney had swallowed a mouthful before he made out the writing on the can: it said WEED-KILLER. However, the water only tasted of rust and rubber.

It was dark in the back of the cave. Stig went to the front where the ashes of a fire were smoking faintly, blew on them, picked up a book that lay beside his bed, tore out a page and rolled it up, lit it at the fire, and carried it to a lamp set in a niche in the wall. As is flared up Barney could see it was in fact an old teapot, filled with some kind of oil, and with a bootlace hanging out of it for a wick.

Extract from 'Stig of the Dump' by Clive King (Puffin 1963). © Clive King, 1963. Reproduced by kind permission of Penguin Books Ltd.

© Andrew Brodie Publications ✓ PO Box 23, Wellington, Somerset, TA21 8YX ✓ www.andrewbrodie.co.uk

Dark Secret

Barnabus relaxed slightly, as he caught sight of the familiar irregular outline of the entrance to his burrow. The welcoming gap between the roots of the great oak tree, meant comfort and safety from the strange smells and noises he had recently detected in the woods. Carefully he pushed aside the overhanging brambles and sniffed the air, checking for unwanted intruders in his burrow. All was as it should be, and Barnabus noticed with satisfaction how the sandy floor had stayed dry and cool throughout the summer storms. He followed the curving run round to its second hidden entrance and was pleased to see that nothing had been disturbed. Back in his sleeping quarters, he cleaned out a dead earthworm that had fallen from the smooth ceiling last night. He noticed, with irritation, the small pile of sand that had collapsed from the inside wall. He scraped and tidied until all was to his satisfaction.

Finally, he was ready to settle down on the pile of dead grass that he had collected over the summer months. As he lay contentedly enveloped in the still darkness, he listened to the noises of the wood drifting towards him. All seemed to be as normal now. The familiar rustling and squeaking of the wood were only the comforting sounds of his near neighbours. He sniffed the air again. It was the same cool, clear air that usually wafted through his burrow, but Barnabus knew that something was not quite right!

© Andrew Brodie Publications ✓ PO Box 23, Wellington, Somerset, TA21 8YX ✓ www.andrewbrodie.co.uk

These questions are about the extract from 'Stig of the Dump'

Choose the best word or words to fit the passage and underline your choice.

1.   According to the passage Stig lives in

    (**a house.**)   (**a cave.**)   (**a tent.**)   (**the woods.**)

2.   Stig kept his den

    (**clean and tidy.**)   (**in a mess.**)

3.   Barney thought that it was a

    (**dreadful**)   (**wonderful**)   place to live.

4.   The second paragraph, beginning with the words, 'He'd never seen..."
    tells us about

    (**fossils and bones.**)   (**the things Barney liked to collect.**)   (**the things inside Stig's den.**)   (**a rubbish dump.**)

5.   Read paragraph 4. Draw a rough sketch of Stig's plumbing system and label it using the information in the paragraph.

6.   Read the extract from 'Dark Secret'. Use the plan on Sheet D to do a comparison of the homes of Stig and Barnabus. Add other headings for yourself. You may like to do a drawing of your impression of what each home looked like inside. Put in as much detail as you can using all the information from the passages and your own comparison.

© Andrew Brodie Publications ✓ PO Box 23, Wellington, Somerset, TA21 8YX ✓ www.andrewbrodie.co.uk

Name   Comparing Texts

Comparing the homes of Stig and Barnabus

	Stig's cave	Barnabus' burrow
Entrance		
Shape		
Walls and floor		
Tidiness and contents		
General feel/comfort		
Fire/smoke		
Other heading of your choice		

© Andrew Brodie Publications ✓ PO Box 23, Wellington, Somerset, TA21 8YX ✓ www.andrewbrodie.co.uk

This unit addresses the Literacy Strategy:
Term 1 objective   12: to comment critically on the language, style, success of examples of non-fiction such as periodicals, reviews, reports, leaflets.
Term 3 objective   15: to secure an understanding of the features of explanatory text from Year 5 term 2 .i.e. to read a range of explanatory texts, investigating and noting features of impersonal style, e.g. complex sentences, use of passive voice, technical vocabulary, hypothetical language (if...then, might, when); use of words/phrases to make sequential, causal, logical connections, e.g. while, during, after, because, due to, etc.

The Church at Thorne St Margaret

The following text shows extracts from a leaflet about a small village church in Somerset.

The church at Thorne is dedicated to St. Margaret, and consists of the nave, south porch, chancel, south aisle, tower and vestry. It is built of hard red sandstone in the Early English style. When the church was restored in 1865 the work was so great that the church was almost rebuilt.

According to Jeboult (1873) before 1865 the nave of the church was very small and the chancel very large. In the old church was a large painting of 'The Flight Into Egypt'. It served for a number of years as a reredos behind the High Altar. Tradition in the village says that in the Pre-Reformation days, the Abbot of Glastonbury would sometimes visit Cothay Manor. The Abbot was very fond of the church at Thorne and while staying at Cothay he would say Mass there whenever he had the opportunity. On such occasions his retinue would be large, these monks would sit in the chancel (hence the large chancel). The Abbot is said to have given the picture of 'The Flight Into Egypt' to the church.

The date of the font is Saxon, one of the oldest fonts in the district. It was thrown out in the churchyard in 1865 after being in use for nearly one thousand years. A new font was installed complete with eight marble pillars. However, the old font has now been restored to its position in the west end of the Church, and might well last another thousand years or so.

The screen forming part of the vestry is one of the ancient ones from the old church.

The windows are in pairs with pointed heads and arcade recesses. The pillars are of Bath stone. The tower is very ancient and formed part of the old church. On the south side is a curious little window with singular tracery. There were three bells in the tower (Jeboult in 1873 says:- 'The tower contains a clock and three bells'). However the Church now only has one bell. It is probable that the two bells and clock were removed during the restoration in 1865 when the other changes took place.

There is a curious old brass taken from the old church, and now fixed to the west wall on the south side of the tower arch. It is an effigy of John Worth, undated (circa 1610), in civil dress, and he is represented as an old man with short curly hair, long beard and moustache. He wears a ruff, doublet, full breeches, gartered stockings and shoes.

© Andrew Brodie Publications ✓ PO Box 23, Wellington, Somerset, TA21 8YX ✓ www.andrewbrodie.co.uk

Name _____ **Thorne St Margaret Church**

Basic Comprehension

1.   When did the restoration of Thorne St Margaret Church take place?

_____

_____

2.   According to the text, who had written about the church in 1873?

_____

_____

3.   According to tradition in the village, what did the Abbot of Glastonbury give to the church?

_____

_____

4.   When was the original font first placed in the Church?

_____

_____

5.   What audience is the leaflet most likely to be aimed at?

_____

_____

_____

6.   Look up the following words and write a description of each one.

   reredos _____

   _____

   retinue _____

   _____

   font _____

   _____

   effigy _____

   _____

Discuss, with a partner, ways in which the writing on the leaflet could be improved.

© Andrew Brodie Publications ✓ PO Box 23, Wellington, Somerset, TA21 8YX ✓ www.andrewbrodie.co.uk

Creating a Leaflet

The Content: Choose a subject that you are familiar with or that you can research easily, e.g. your school, town or village, place of worship, local museum or a club that you attend.

Preparation: Prepare by researching the information you are going to use. You may include a map, interview a relevant person, search the internet, visit the site, take photographs or use the library.

Vocabulary and Tenses: Look at the extract from the leaflet of Thorne St Margaret Church and any other leaflets you have seen. The present tense is used most dominantly and the language is passive and contains no opinions or views. This is called passive voice. You should write in an appropriate style to suit your audience and purpose and use technical or specific vocabulary where necessary.

Paragraphs: Organise your information into about 5 paragraphs each with a clear introductory sentence which should indicate what the rest of the paragraph is about.

Sentences: Use a variety of sentence lengths including structures to express ideas clearly and maintain interest.

Layout: The basic writing frame can be used to produce a handwritten '3 fold' leaflet with illustrations drawn or pasted on. Cut out the leaflet frame, then fold along the two fold lines. You will then be able to work on both sides of the leaflet. Alternatively the frame can be used as a draft for your work which can later be word processed and photographs scanned or pasted on.

© Andrew Brodie Publications ✓ PO Box 23, Wellington, Somerset, TA21 8YX ✓ www.andrewbrodie.co.uk

Subject:

© Andrew Brodie Publications ✓ PO Box 23, Wellington, Somerset, TA21 8YX ✓ www.andrewbrodie.co.uk

This unit addresses the Literacy Strategy:
Term 2 objective   15: to recognise how arguments are constructed to be effective, through, e.g. the expression, sequence and linking of points; the provision of persuasive examples, illustrations and evidence; pre-empting or answering potential objections; appealing to the known views and feelings of the audience.
Term 3 objective   16: to identify the key features of impersonal formal language, e.g. the present tense, the passive voice and discuss when and why they are used.
Term 3 objective   17: to appraise a text quickly and effectively, to retrieve information from it; to find information quickly and evaluate its value.

New Lanark 2

Not far from the city of Edinburgh in Scotland is the small town of Lanark. The River Clyde flows through Lanark on its way to the city of Glasgow and the Irish Sea beyond.

In approximately 1785 a man called David Dale began the construction of giant water mills alongside the fast flowing River Clyde. The mills were carefully designed to make use of the power of the water to drive machinery. The machines were built especially to spin cotton.

By 1793 there were over one thousand people employed to work in the mills. Whole streets of houses had to be built to accommodate them all. The area became known as New Lanark.

Looking back as we are now from the twenty-first century, what we find strange is that the vast majority of New Lanark's workforce was made up of children. Nearly eight hundred of the one thousand, one hundred and fifty-seven employees were children – this number even included five six-year-olds, thirty-three seven-year-olds, seventy-one eight-year-olds and ninety-five nine-year-olds. Many of these children were orphans and had to sleep in huge dormitories. This is how David Dale described their living conditions:

There are six sleeping apartments for them, and three children are allowed to each bed. The ceilings and walls of the apartments are whitewashed twice a year with hot lime and the floors washed in scalding hot water and sand. The children sleep on wooden-bottomed beds on bed ticks filled with straw which is in general changed once a month. A sheet covers the bed ticks and above that there are one or two pairs of blankets and a bed cover as the season requires. The bedrooms are carefully swept and the windows thrown open every morning in which state they remain through the day. Of late, cast iron beds have been introduced in place of wooden ones. The upper body clothing in use in summer both for boys and girls is entirely of cotton which, as they have spare suits to change with, are washed once a fortnight. In winter the boys are dressed in woollen cloth and they, as well as the girls, have complete dress suits for Sundays. Their linens are changed once a week. For a few months in summer boys and girls go without shoes and stockings.   Extract from 'The Story of New Lanark' reproduced by kind permission of the New Lanark Conservation Trust.

© Andrew Brodie Publications ✓ PO Box 23, Wellington, Somerset, TA21 8YX ✓ www.andrewbrodie.co.uk

Strange as it may seem to us now, these children were very fortunate compared to many. They had to work long hours but they were provided with good food and clean, dry accommodation.

In other mills throughout Britain, the child workers often had to live in appalling conditions.

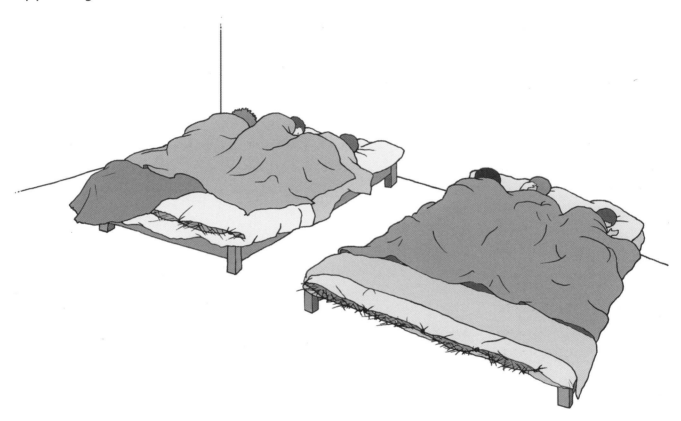

David Dale's daughter Caroline, married a young Welshman called Robert Owen. He became the manager of the New Lanark mills and introduced the greatest improvements in conditions for the children. The most significant improvement was the opening of a brand new school in 1816. All children up to the age of about eleven no longer had to work in the mills but attended school instead. Older children were allowed to attend in the evening, after their day at work.

Extract from 'The Story of New Lanark' reproduced by kind permission of the New Lanark Conservation Trust.

New Lanark is now a working museum. It is a very interesting place to visit. You might also like to visit the website. **www.newlanark.org/kids**

© Andrew Brodie Publications ✓ PO Box 23, Wellington, Somerset, TA21 8YX ✓ www.andrewbrodie.co.uk

Put a ring around each correct answer:

1. New Lanark is situated next to the River

    Lanark.   Clyde.   Thames.   Dale.

2. The mills derived their power from

    water.   wind.   electricity.   gas.

3. The mills were used to spin

    wool.   steel.   flour.   cotton.

4. New Lanark is in

    Scotland.   England.   Wales.   Ireland.

The sentences below provide a summary of the passage, including a title. In your exercise book, rewrite the sentences in the correct order.

- Most of the workers in New Lanark were children.

- The purpose of the mills was for the spinning of cotton.

- Robert Owen became the new manager of the mills.

- The Story of New Lanark

- By 1793 there were over one thousand employees.

- David Dale began building giant mills alongside the River Clyde in about 1785.

- He opened a new school in 1816 and young children no longer had to work in the mills.

© Andrew Brodie Publications ✓ PO Box 23, Wellington, Somerset, TA21 8YX ✓ www.andrewbrodie.co.uk

David Dale's description of the children's living conditions was given in a letter to the Manchester Board of Health. Give three examples of sentences or phrases from his description that show he was seeking to convince the Board of Health that there were high standards of hygiene.

_____

_____

_____

_____

_____

_____

_____

_____

We might not consider these to be high levels of hygiene by today's standards. Imagine that David Dale's description had been written this week. Write a reply to him stating why you feel that the standards are not good enough. Consider all the points that he has listed in his description. Set your reply out as a formal letter. Use a sheet of plain paper with a line guide or write your reply on a computer.

Manchester Board of Health
High Road
Manchester
MA12 2QN

Mr David Dale
New Lanark Mills
Lanark

17 September 2003

Dear Mr Dale,

Thank you for your letter regarding the conditions that you provide for the children who work at New Lanark. Our committee has some concerns ………

……
Yours sincerely,

…………

© Andrew Brodie Publications ✔ PO Box 23, Wellington, Somerset, TA21 8YX ✔ www.andrewbrodie.co.uk

This unit addresses the Literacy Strategy:
Term 3 objective   17: to appraise a text quickly and effectively, to retrieve information from it; to find information quickly and evaluate its value.
Term 3 objective   18: to secure the skills of skimming, scanning and efficient reading so that research is fast and effective.

YEAR **6** | UNIT **23** | Sheet **A**   Name   Forty Fabulous Facts

On these 2 pages you will find 40 facts.

You will be given 20 minutes to answer questions about them.

✳ In the 20 minutes you have been given have a quick look through the facts and then begin to answer the questions.

✳ The questions must be answered correctly from the facts in the text. (Not from any other general knowledge you may have.)

✳ This unit encourages you to look at a text to find information quickly and efficiently.

✳ Looking for key words relevant to each question will help you to find information, as will looking under the correct sub-headings.

✳   After 20 minutes you will be stopped, so you can find out how many questions you have answered correctly. Your teacher may then give you time to finish them all.

✳ HAVE FUN!

Forty Fabulous Facts

PLACES

1.   The state of Louisiana in the U.S.A. was originally a French colony, and was named in honour of King Louis XIV.

2.   The North Pole was first reached by man in 1909.

3.   The South Pole was first reached by man in 1911.

4.   The Maldives are a group of about 1000 small islands in the Indian Ocean. Most are uninhabited.

5.   The island of Sri Lanka is off southern India. It used to be known as Ceylon.

6.   Lowestoft is the most easterly town in England.

7.   Vancouver is a city on the western coast of Canada, whilst Quebec is on the eastern side of the same country.

8.   The highest mountain in New Zealand is Mount Cook.

9.   Kenya is a country in East Africa, its capital city is Nairobi.

10.   Antigua, Montserrat, Aruba, Grenada and St Lucia are all islands in the Caribbean.

11.   Kuala Lumpur is the capital city of Malaysia.

12.   Delhi is the capital of India.

© Andrew Brodie Publications ✓ PO Box 23, Wellington, Somerset, TA21 8YX ✓ www.andrewbrodie.co.uk

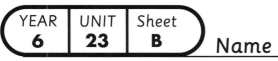 MUSIC

13. A standard size piano keyboard has 88 notes. (Some black and some white.)
14. The piano was originally known as the 'pianoforte', literally meaning 'softloud'.
15. Orchestras, whatever their size, all have four main sections: strings, woodwind, brass and percussion.
16. The largest (and lowest sounding) instrument in the string section is the double bass, and in the brass section it is the tuba.
17. The saxophone was invented by 'Adolphe Sax' in 1846.
18. The sousaphone was designed by John Philip Sousa in 1898
19. The musical sound of pealing church bells was begun in England during the Middle Ages.

  GENERAL KNOWLEDGE

20. An okapi is an African animal related to the giraffe.
21. More than 40,000 years ago people made whistles from the bones of reindeer toes.
22. On the moon a person would only weigh about one sixth of their weight on earth. This is because earth's gravity is six times greater.
23. Glass is made by heating sand, soda and limestone.
24. Our planet is thought to be more than four thousand five hundred million years old.
25. Spiders belong to the arachnid family.
26. Starfish belong to the echinoderm family.
27. Crabs and lobsters belong to the crustacean family.
28. An Italian called Guglielmo Marconi made the very first radio in 1894.
29. Glaciers are slowly moving rivers of ice.
30. Fjords are created by glaciers. They have very steep sides.
31. Flint was used to make some of the first tools known to man.
32. The first electrically operated vacuum cleaner was made in 1908 by William Hoover.
33. The colours of the rainbow are Red, Orange, Yellow, Green, Blue, Indigo and Violet. They are always seen in that order with red at the top and violet at the bottom.
34. More than three quarters of the earth's surface is covered by water.
35. Earthquakes are measured by an instrument called a seismograph.
36. Fossils are rocks that contain the impression of a plant or animal and can be many millions of years old.
37. The first mass produced car was the Model T Ford. More than 15 million of these were sold during its production from 1908 to 1927.
38. Jakob and Wilhelm Grimm wrote many fairy tales including 'Snow White' and 'Rapunzel'.
39. Marco Polo took four years to travel across Asia (along a route known as the Silk Road) going from Europe to China.
40. Neil Armstrong was the first man to stand on the moon. He did this in July 1969.

© Andrew Brodie Publications ✓ PO Box 23, Wellington, Somerset, TA21 8YX ✓ www.andrewbrodie.co.uk

Basic Comprehension

Answer the 30 questions as quickly and carefully as you can.

The questions get slightly trickier towards the end.

1. Which American state was named in honour of Louis XIV of France?

    _____

2. What is heated to make glass? _____

3. In what year did Guglielmo Marconi make the first radio?

    _____

4. When did man first reach the South Pole? _____

5. How many Model T Fords were sold? _____

6. How many sections are there in an orchestra? _____

7. Name the sections.

    _____

8. Nairobi is the capital of which African country? _____

9. What was made in the early 20th century by William Hoover?

    _____

10. Name three islands in the Caribbean.

    _____

11. To which 'family' do spiders belong? _____

12. What name is the island once known as Ceylon now called?

    _____

13. What is an okapi? _____

14. How much of the earth's surface is covered by water?

    _____

15. What instrument would you use to measure an earthquake?

    _____

Name   Forty Fabulous Facts

16. What stone was used by man to make some of the very first tools?

     _____

17. For what did people once use reindeer toe bones?

     _____

18. If I weigh ten kilograms on the moon, approximately how much would
     I weigh on earth?   _____

19. Name a member of the echinoderm family   _____

20. In which country would you find Mount Cook?   _____

21. How many islands are there in the Maldives?   _____

22. What name is given to a slowly moving ice river?   _____

23. Which musical instrument was designed in 1898 and by whom?

     _____

24. What musical sound was first heard in England in the Middle Ages?

     _____

25. Who wrote the story of Rapunzel?

     _____

26. Name the colours of the rainbow. Start with the colour seen at the
     bottom of the rainbow and end with the one at the top.

     _____   _____   _____   _____

     _____   _____   _____

27. Where would you find the city of Quebec? _____

28. Is the earth believed to be more or less than twenty million years old?

     _____

29. Name the route taken by Marco Polo from Europe to China.

     _____

30. Is the town of Lowestoft on the coast or inland?

     _____

How many questions did you answer correctly in the time given?

© Andrew Brodie Publications ✓ PO Box 23, Wellington, Somerset, TA21 8YX ✓ www.andrewbrodie.co.uk

This unit addresses the Literacy Strategy:
Term 1 objective 11: to distinguish between biography and autobiography.
Term 1 objective 12: to comment critically on the language, style, success of examples of non-fiction such as periodicals, reviews, reports, leaflets.
Term 3 objective 19: to review a range of non-fiction text types and their characteristics, discussing when a writer might choose to write in a given style and form.

Here are some more extracts from the magazine..

Weather Watch.

Enjoy finding out more about wind, rain and storms,
from our resident Meteorologist, Ivor Forecast.

DID YOU KNOW...

'Nimbus' comes from the latin word for rain, hence nimbostratus and cumulonimbus clouds bring rain.

Lightning is seen before thunder is heard, as light travels faster than sound.

Lightning will always try to find the easiest way to the ground. Tall buildings, church spires and isolated trees are often struck. This is why it is very unwise to shelter under a tree, most especially if the tree is very tall or standing in an isolated position.

Thunderstorms usually occur in hot weather.

Wind has been used by man to power windmills and sailing boats for hundreds of years. More recently wind turbines have been built to generate electricity.

The Beaufort Scale is a way of measuring and describing the force of the wind. It ranges from force 0 (completely calm) to force 12 (hurricane).

A weather vane always points into the wind so that you know what direction the wind is coming from.

In tropical areas, late summer is sometimes known as hurricane season, as that is when hurricane winds can be in excess of 200 miles per hour. If an island or coastal area is unlucky enough to be hit by a hurricane much damage is done and lives can be lost.

© Andrew Brodie Publications ✓ PO Box 23, Wellington, Somerset, TA21 8YX ✓ www.andrewbrodie.co.uk

Letters to the EDITOR

If your letter is printed we will send you your own junior meteorologist kit including a thermometer, rain gauge, wind vane, cloud recognition cards and the exclusive 'Weather Watch' record book.

Our **STAR LETTER** will also receive our special waterproof 'Weather Watch' camera to ensure you do not miss any interesting phenomena you may see.

Dear Editor
In the area where I live, there have been several floods during the past five years. I believe that global warming is responsible for this and that every government throughout the world should be aiming to cut emissions caused by use of fossil fuels.
As younger people we should all play a part in the protection of our world. If we live near enough to our schools we should walk or cycle there to reduce the use of cars. Simply remembering to turn off lights as we left rooms would also help.
I would like to urge all 'Weather Watch' readers to be aware of our global problems and do all they can to protect our future.

Yours sincerely
I.M. Concerned.

STAR LETTER!

Dear Editor and fellow Weather Watchers,
I have been collecting common folklore sayings concerning weather and weather forecasting. I should be grateful if you could include an article on this subject in a future issue. It would be of great interest to me, and hopefully many of your readers to know more about this subject particularly which of these sayings are actually correct - do cows really lie down when rain is on the way?
Yours hopefully
U.R. Raining.

Dear Editor,
I wish to tell you, and all the Weather Watch readers, my thoughts on global warming. Over millions of years our earth has had a fluctuating climate and I believe that the current rise in temperature is no more than a normal climatic deviation. I do not think we can really do anything to change the situation and should simply learn to live with it. Perhaps before long we will instead be heading towards another ice age!
Yours sincerely
I.C.Weather.

© Andrew Brodie Publications ✓ PO Box 23, Wellington, Somerset, TA21 8YX ✓ www.andrewbrodie.co.uk

YEAR	UNIT	Sheet
6	**24**	**C**

Name

More from
Weather Watch

Basic Comprehension

☀ What do you notice about the name of the meteorologist and the names of the letter writers?

_____

_____

☀ What does a meteorologist do?

_____

_____

☀ Which way does a weather vane always point?

_____

_____

☀ Name the items included in 'Weather Watch' junior meteorologist kit.

_____

_____

☀ What extra item is sent to the writer of the star letter?

_____

☀ Write a simple definition for each of the following words from the articles.

fluctuating _____

_____

thermometer _____

_____

global _____

_____

isolated _____

_____

☀ Is the '**Did you know?**' article opinion, fact or fiction?   _____

☀ Is the letter from **I. M. Concerned** opinion, fact or fiction?   _____

☀ On the back of the sheet make a list of all the weather sayings you know of. You may wish to work with a partner to do this.

© Andrew Brodie Publications ✓ PO Box 23, Wellington, Somerset, TA21 8YX ✓ www.andrewbrodie.co.uk

Advanced Comprehension

☀ In the '**Did you know?**' feature which tense is mainly used (i.e. past, present, future)?

_____

☀ Why do you think it has been written this way?

_____

_____

☀ Do you think the '**Did you know?**' facts could have been written in a more
   meaningful order? Explain your answer.

_____

_____

_____

_____

☀ Read the letter from **I. M. Concerned** to the editor. With a friend discuss its
   strengths and weaknesses. In the box below make notes on your
   discussion, ready to share with the class.

S T R E N G T H S	W E A K N E S S E S

☀ Give three reasons why you might consider the letter from **I. C. Weathe**r
   to be a weak one.

_____

_____

_____

☀ For each of the following words taken from the 'Weather Watch' articles, ring the one
   that has the closest meaning to it from the choices given.

deviation -	disturbance	variation	digression	expression
measuring -	assessing	pushing	viewing	quantifying
generate -	produce	genial	cause	aid

☀ Use the back of the sheet to write a short, well-constructed letter to the editor stating
   your views on the way our climate is changing.

© Andrew Brodie Publications ✓ PO Box 23, Wellington, Somerset, TA21 8YX ✓ www.andrewbrodie.co.uk

We hope that you have found this book useful. We would be very pleased to receive your comments on this book or to hear your suggestions for new books. If you wish to make any comments or if you would like to be put on our mailing list please contact us:

by telephone: **01823 665493**

by fax: **01823 665345**

by email: **feedback@andrewbrodie.co.uk**

by post: **Andrew Brodie Publications**
PO Box 23
Wellington
Somerset
TA21 8YX

You may wish to photocopy and fax this page to us, completing any of the sections below that you feel relevant:

Name: _____

Address: _____

_____

Telephone: _____

Email address: _____

Comments: _____

_____

_____

_____

_____

© Andrew Brodie Publications ✓ PO Box 23, Wellington, Somerset, TA21 8YX ✓ www.andrewbrodie.co.uk